REVISE BTEC NATIONAL
Children's Play, Learning and Development

REVISION WORKBOOK

Series Consultant: Harry Smith

Author: Brenda Baker

Unit 4 research structure: Georgina Shaw

While the publishers have made every attempt to ensure that advice on the qualification and its assessment is accurate, the official specification and associated assessment guidance materials are the only authoritative source of information and should always be referred to for definitive guidance.

This qualification is reviewed on a regular basis and may be updated in the future. Any such updates that affect the content of this Revision Workbook will be outlined at www.pearsonfe.co.uk/BTECchanges.

A note from the publisher

In order to ensure that this resource offers high-quality support for the associated Pearson qualification, it has been through a review process by the awarding body. This process confirms that this resource fully covers the teaching and learning content of the specification or part of a specification at which it is aimed. It also confirms that it demonstrates an appropriate balance between the development of subject skills, knowledge and understanding, in addition to preparation for assessment.

Endorsement does not cover any guidance on assessment activities or processes (e.g. practice questions or advice on how to answer assessment questions), included in the resource nor does it prescribe any particular approach to the teaching or delivery of a related course.

Pearson examiners have not contributed to any sections in this resource relevant to examination papers for which they had prior responsibility.

Examiners will not use endorsed resources as a source of material for any assessment set by Pearson.

Endorsement of a resource does not mean that the resource is required to achieve this Pearson qualification, nor does it mean that it is the only suitable material available to support the qualification, and any resource lists produced by the awarding body shall include this and other appropriate resources.

For the full range of Pearson revision titles across KS2, KS3, GCSE, Functional Skills, AS/A Level and BTEC visit: www.pearsonschools.co.uk/revise

Published by Pearson Education Limited, 80 Strand, London, WC2R 0RL.

www.pearsonschoolsandfecolleges.co.uk

Copies of official specifications for all Pearson qualifications may be found on the website: qualifications.pearson.com

Text and illustrations © Pearson Education Limited 2017
Typeset and illustrations by Kamae Design, Oxford
Produced by Out of House Publishing
Cover illustration © Miriam Sturdee

The right of Brenda Baker to be identified as author of this work has been asserted by her in accordance with the Copyright, Designs and Patents Act 1988.

First published 2017

20 19 18 17
10 9 8 7 6 5 4 3 2 1

British Library Cataloguing in Publication Data

A catalogue record for this book is available from the British Library

ISBN 978 1 292 23057 3

Acknowledgements

We are grateful to the following for permission to reproduce copyright material:

Text
Article on page 51 from Childcare Sufficiency and Sustainability in Disadvantaged Areas DFE-RB246, September 2012 Sarah Dickens, Ivonne Wollny and Eleanor Ireland. Crown Copyright: contains public sector information licensed under the Open Government Licence v3.0; Extract on page 64 from Gibb, J. et al, 2011. Rolling out free education for disadvantaged two year olds: an implementation study for local authorities and providers. Contains public sector information licensed under the Open Government Licence v3.0. Extract on page 50, 62, 65, 67, 68, 70 to 72 from SAMTAB (source, appearance, method, timeliness, applicability, balance) - method for completion for assessing suitability of sources, Georgina Shaw with permission.

Notes from the publisher
1.
In order to ensure that this resource offers high-quality support for the associated Pearson qualification, it has been through a review process by the awarding body. This process confirms that this resource fully covers the teaching and learning content of the specification or part of a specification at which it is aimed. It also confirms that it demonstrates an appropriate balance between the development of subject skills, knowledge and understanding, in addition to preparation for assessment.

Endorsement does not cover any guidance on assessment activities or processes (e.g. practice questions or advice on how to answer assessment questions), included in the resource nor does it prescribe any particular approach to the teaching or delivery of a related course.

While the publishers have made every attempt to ensure that advice on the qualification and its assessment is accurate, the official specification and associated assessment guidance materials are the only authoritative source of information and should always be referred to for definitive guidance.

Pearson examiners have not contributed to any sections in this resource relevant to examination papers for which they have responsibility.

Examiners will not use endorsed resources as a source of material for any assessment set by Pearson.

Endorsement of a resource does not mean that the resource is required to achieve this Pearson qualification, nor does it mean that it is the only suitable material available to support the qualification, and any resource lists produced by the awarding body shall include this and other appropriate resources.

2.
Pearson has robust editorial processes, including answer and fact checks, to ensure the accuracy of the content in this publication, and every effort is made to ensure this publication is free of errors. We are, however, only human, and occasionally errors do occur. Pearson is not liable for any misunderstandings that arise as a result of errors in this publication, but it is our priority to ensure that the content is accurate. If you spot an error, please do contact us at resourcescorrections@pearson.com so we can make sure it is corrected.

Websites
Pearson Education Limited is not responsible for the content of any external internet sites. It is essential for tutors to preview each website before using it in class so as to ensure that the URL is still accurate, relevant and appropriate. We suggest that tutors bookmark useful websites and consider enabling students to access them through the school/college intranet.

Introduction

This Workbook has been designed to help you revise the skills you may need for the externally assessed units of your course. Remember that you won't necessarily be studying all the units included here – it will depend on the qualification you are taking.

BTEC National Qualification	Externally assessed units
For the following three qualifications: Extended Certificate Foundation Diploma Diploma	1 Children's Development 2 Development of Children's Communication, Literacy and Numeracy Skills
Extended Diploma	1 Children's Development 2 Development of Children's Communication, Literacy and Numeracy Skills 4 Enquiries into Current Research in Early Years Practice

Your Workbook

Each unit in this Workbook contains either one or two sets of revision questions or revision tasks, to help you **revise the skills** you may need in your assessment. The selected content, outcomes, questions and answers used in each unit are provided to help you to revise content and ways of applying your skills. Ask your tutor or check the Pearson website for the most up-to-date **Sample Assessment Material** and **Mark Schemes** to get an indication of the structure of your actual assessment and what this requires of you. The detail of the actual assessment may change so always make sure you are up to date.

This Workbook will often include one or more useful features that explain or break down longer questions or tasks. Remember that these features won't appear in your actual assessment!

> Grey boxes like this contain **hints and tips** about ways that you might complete a task, interpret a brief, understand a concept or structure your responses.

 This icon will appear next to an **example partial answer** to a revision question or revision task. You should read the partial answer carefully, then complete it in your own words.

> This is a revision activity. It will help you understand some of the skills needed to complete the revision task or question.

> These boxes will tell you where you can find more help in Pearson's BTEC National Revision Guide. Visit **www.pearsonschools.co.uk/revise** for more information.

There is often space on the pages for you to write in. However, if you are carrying out research and making ongoing notes, you may want to use separate paper. Similarly, some units will be assessed through submission of digital files, or on screen, rather than on paper. Ask your tutor or check the Pearson website for the most up-to-date details.

Contents

Unit 1: Children's Development

1   Your exam

2   Revision paper 1 (guided)

14   Revision paper 2

Unit 2: Development of Children's Communication, Literacy and Numeracy Skills

24   Your set task

25   Revision task (guided)

Unit 4: Enquiries into Current Research in Early Years Practice

49   Your set task

50   Revision task (guided)

89   Answers

A small bit of small print

Pearson publishes Sample Assessment Material and the Specification on its website. This is the official content and this book should be used in conjunction with it. The questions and revision tasks in this book have been written to help you practise the knowledge and skills you will require for your assessment. Remember: the real assessment may not look like this.

Unit 1: Children's Development

Your exam

Unit 1 will be assessed through an exam, which will be set by Pearson. You will need to use your understanding of children's developmental progress from birth up to seven years 11 months. Questions will assess your understanding of how the principles, theories and models of development apply to individual children. Scenario-based questions will assess your ability to apply theory to practical, real-life situations and long-answer questions will assess your ability to analyse and interpret theories, how they relate to other domains of development and their impact on early years practice.

Your Revision Workbook

This Workbook is designed to **revise skills** that might be needed in your exam. The details of the actual exam may change so always make sure you are up to date. Ask your tutor or check the **Pearson website** for the most up-to-date **Sample Assessment Material** to get an indication of the structure of your exam and what this requires of you.

To support your revision, this Workbook contains revision questions to help you revise the skills that might be needed in your exam.

Responding to scenarios

When reading **scenarios** and answering questions based on them, make sure you read the information carefully. Scenarios use **realistic situations** and **contexts** such as family background, age, skills and abilities, additional needs, environment or transitions.

In response to the scenarios you may apply knowledge and understanding about:

- principles of growth and development
- patterns of physical, cognitive, emotional and social development from birth up to the age of 7 years 11 months
- factors that impact on children's growth and development
- theories that help to explain early years practice
- how early years practitioners can promote and support children's growth and development.

Answering types of questions

There is guidance in this Workbook for the skills involved in answering the following types of questions:

Describe   Explain   Which   Give   List

Identify   Discuss   Assess   Analyse   Evaluate

Links To help you revise skills that might be needed in your Unit 1 exam, this Workbook contains two sets of revision questions starting on pages 2 and 14. The first is guided and models good techniques to help you develop your skills. The second gives you the opportunity to apply the skills you have developed. See the introduction on page iii for more information on features included to help you revise.

Revision paper 1

To support your revision, this Workbook contains revision questions to help you revise the skills that might be needed in your exam. The details of the actual exam may change so always make sure you are up to date. Ask your tutor or check the Pearson website for the most up-to-date Sample Assessment Material.

SECTION A

Answer ALL questions. Write your answers in the spaces provided.

Some questions must be answered with a cross in a box ☒. If you change your mind about an answer, put a line through the box ☒ and then mark your new answer with a cross ☒.

1 Claire and Vincent have three children:
- Jack, who is 11 months old
- Ruby, who is 3 years old
- Sam, who is almost 5 years old.

The children are growing and developing well. Jack stays at home with Claire. Ruby has just started nursery. Ruby has met her expected milestones in all areas of development and has advanced skills in her speech and language development. This has helped her to make friends easily. Sam is doing well in the reception class at school. He can count to 20 accurately and is already using numbers to solve problems involving addition to 10, and sharing.

(a) Which aspect of Jack's fine motor skills is expected by the time he is 12 months old? `1 mark`

☐ **A** Is able to turn single pages of a picture book

☐ **B** Can hold a rattle for a few seconds

☐ **C** Feeds himself using a spoon and fork

☐ **D** Picks up a bead using a pincer grasp

> If answering **'Which'** questions, select the correct item or feature from a definite set. Put a cross in one box ☒ to indicate your answer. If you change your mind, put a line through it and then put a cross in another box.

(b) Identify **three** possible features of Ruby's physical development at her age. `3 marks`

> If answering **'Identify'** questions, recall your knowledge of the principles but do not give further explanation.
> - Add a feature of Ruby's fine motor skills at her age.
> - If the question does not specify gross or fine motor skills, try to include at least one example for each type.

1   Ruby will be able to pedal a tricycle.

2   Ruby will be able to balance when walking along a line.

3   ....

🔗 **Links**   Look at pages 8–9 of the Revision Guide to revise fine and gross motor skills.

(c) Describe **two** theories of language and communication that help to explain Ruby's language development.

4 marks

1   Chomsky's theory is based on the belief that language development is predetermined. He called this the Language Acquisition Device (LAD). This means that Ruby will

> If answering **'Describe'** questions, give a **clear account** that shows **knowledge** of the facts and **main features** of the topic.

....

....

2   Skinner's operant conditioning theory is based on a belief that ....

....

Ruby's advanced language skills may mean ....

....

(d) Discuss how early years practitioners may use Vygotsky's cognitive theory to promote Sam's numeracy development.

8 marks

It is important that early years practitioners have assessed Sam's stage of numeracy development. Vygotsky refers to this as the Zone of Actual Development. Knowing what Sam can already do will help practitioners to plan how best to support Sam to reach the next stage. For instance, he can already add numbers to 10 so he could be helped to work with higher numbers and to look at patterns in numbers such as counting in twos or tens.

> Go on to give an overview of Vygotsky's theory that describes the role of the adult to support children's learning. Discuss the role of Sam as the apprentice and explore the importance of the adult in working alongside Sam to model learning, pose questions and encourage thinking in ways he may not do himself. You could give examples to support your ideas.

Vygotsky refers to the next stage as the Zone of ....

....

....

....

....

....

....

....

....

....

Links Look at page 17 of the Revision Guide to revise Vygotsky and page 22 to revise Chomsky and Skinner.

Total for Question 1 = 16 marks

2 Powel is aged 3½ years and Sofia is aged 18 months. They live with their mother, Roza. The family moved to the UK 6 months ago. Roza now has a job as a care assistant so Sofia and Powel have just started nursery.

Sofia's and Powel's key person, Helen, invited Roza and the children into the nursery a week before the start date. She spent time talking to Roza to find out about the children's needs and interests. On the first day at nursery, Sofia was very upset when her mother left, and ran to her crying as soon as she returned. After a few days she was happy to be left with her key person.

Powel speaks Polish at home and has only a few words of English. He tried to play with other children but got frustrated easily and often snatched toys from them.

> **Guided**

(a) Give **two** reasons why Powel may have shown frustration.

2 marks

1 Powel may find it difficult to control his emotions because he is in an unfamiliar environment.

2 ....

> If answering **'Give'** questions, give brief examples or a justification (reason) for something. Think about the effect on Powel if he is unable to express himself in English.

> **Guided**

(b) Identify **two** ways that early years practitioners can support Powel's communication skills.

2 marks

1 Practitioners could use pictures of ....

> Think of the importance of non-verbal communication for this answer.

....

2 ....

....

(c) Describe **two** ways that attachment theories may help to explain Sofia's behaviour.

4 marks

> Write one or two sentences about Bowlby's attachment theory to explain the importance of Sofia having a strong bond with her mother for building future attachments. Write one or two sentences which link to Ainsworth's attachment styles the way Sofia behaves when her mother left her at nursery and returned later.

1 ....

....

2 ....

....

> **Links** Look at page 24 of the Revision Guide to revise communication and page 32 to revise attachment theories.

(d) Discuss how Bronfenbrenner's bio-ecological systems theory helps to explain the importance of the environment on Powel's and Sofia's growth and development.

8 marks

Bronfenbrenner's bio-ecological systems theory should be discussed in this answer.

In your discussion consider:

- the **influence** of Powel's and Sofia's immediate environments and the people who care for them (microsystem)
- the **importance** of the relationship between the nursery and home described in the scenario (mesosystem)
- how the timing of **transitions**, e.g. starting nursery after just moving to the UK, may affect development (chronosystem).

....

....

....

....

....

....

....

....

....

....

....

....

....

....

....

....

Links Look at page 31 of the Revision Guide to revise Bronfenbrenner's theory.

Total for Question 2 = 16 marks

3 | Jasmine has one child, Amy, aged 4 years and has just found that she is 6 weeks pregnant. Amy goes to a childminder while her mother works part time as a cleaner. Amy is due to start reception class at school in September. Jasmine finds it difficult to buy suitable foods on her wage and sometimes uses food banks. Jasmine likes to smoke because she says it reduces her stress, but she does not do this indoors. She used to drink alcohol regularly but has now reduced her intake to the recommended levels.

Amy was 4 weeks premature and is still small for her age. She enjoys looking at books and recognises a few words. She uses a palmar grasp to colour pictures. The childminder also looks after two other children, who are $3\frac{1}{2}$ years old. Amy loves to join in with their play. She can cooperate with them in domestic play and can take turns in games. The childminder often takes the children to the park. Amy likes the swings and can hold on to the first level on the climbing frame while the others climb to the top.

(a) Give **one** example that indicates that Amy's physical development is not meeting the norms for her age.

2 marks

....

....

....

> You could give one example of gross motor or one example of fine motor development.

> **Guided**

(b) List **two** ways that Jasmine's lifestyle may affect the growth and development of her unborn baby.

2 marks

1 Lack of a nutritious diet.

2 ....

> If answering **'List'** questions, give an item-by-item record.

> **Guided**

(c) Describe **two** ways that the delay in Amy's physical development may affect her ability to take part in school activities.

4 marks

> Make sure that you explain how delays in both gross and fine motor skills may affect Amy. For example, she will need to use the large muscles in her body to take part in active play and fine, manipulative skills for dressing and art activities and skills.

Amy will need ....

to be able to take part in physical play activity with friends. If she lacks these skills it may affect

her ....

....

Amy will need ....

to be able to ....

....

....

....

....

> **Links** Look at pages 8–9 of the Revision Guide to revise fine and gross motor skills.

Guided >

(d) Discuss the importance of early recognition of Amy's atypical development.

[8 marks]

> If answering **'Discuss'** questions, explore all the different aspects of the topic, considering how the different factors interrelate and their importance in their influence on the developing child.

Continuous assessment is important to recognise when a child is not reaching their expected

growth or developmental milestones. Once it has been recognised that Amy is not meeting

expected norms in her physical development, practitioners can work together with Jasmine to

....

Assessment may indicate health problems or genetic conditions that require specialist treatment.

Early recognition can ....

....

Delayed development in one area may impact on other areas of development. It may affect Amy's

emotional and social development because ....

....

....

Her cognitive development could also be affected if ....

....

....

The earlier that support is put into place by practitioners and, if necessary, specialists, the more

likely it ....

....

> **Links** Look at page 6 of the Revision Guide to revise atypical development.

Total for Question 3 = 16 marks

4 Matthew and Diane have two children: Sean, aged 6 years and Sara, aged 2 years. The family is waiting to be rehoused. They rent a small two-bedroomed house that has no outdoor space. The house is damp and many of the houses nearby have already been demolished. The area has lots of waste ground where people dump rubbish. Matthew has just been made redundant from his job as a security guard. Sean is an active child with good physical skills and he gets frustrated that he can't play outside. He is doing well at school and is meeting his milestones in language and literacy. He has started hitting friends if he can't get his own way so they have started excluding him from their games. After Sara was born, Diane had a period of depression and went into hospital for two weeks. Sara was looked after by an aunt. Sara has just started playgroup but gets so distressed each time she is left that Diane is considering keeping her at home.

(a) Which area of Sean's development has been mostly affected by the family's situation? **1 mark**

- ☐ **A** Physical
- ☐ **B** Emotional
- ☐ **C** Cognitive
- ☐ **D** Social

> **Guided**

(b) Give **three** justifications why the family should be rehoused. **3 marks**

> Think of the effects on the family of cramped living conditions and the importance for children of having access to outdoor space.

1 Damp is likely to cause ill health, affecting growth and development.

2 ....

....

3 ....

....

> **Guided**

(c) Explain (giving **two** reasons) how Bowlby's attachment theory helps to explain Sara's behaviour. **4 marks**

> If answering '**Explain**' questions, demonstrate that you can **apply** your understanding of the subject and context of the question by **giving reasons to support** your opinions, views or argument. If you use terms such as 'because', 'this means that' or 'as', it will help ensure that you give a reason.

1 According to Bowlby, the first few weeks are critical for forming attachments with the mother.

Separation at that time can affect Sara's .... development.

2 Bowlby suggests that poor attachments with the primary carer can affect how children form

....

This means that ....

> **Links** Look at page 32 of the Revision Guide to revise attachment theory.

(d) Discuss how Sean's emotional development may impact on his holistic development. [8 marks]

> Think about the effects on Sean's:
> · **self-esteem** and how it may affect his interest in learning
> · **confidence** in his own physical abilities
> · **isolation**.

Sean is showing through his behaviour that the family's situation may have affected his emotions. If he is having difficulty in coping with his feelings, it can cause sleeping or eating problems. This can have an impact on Sean's health, growth and development.

....

....

....

....

....

....

....

....

....

....

....

....

....

....

....

Links Look at page 28 of the Revision Guide to revise emotional development.

Total for Question 4 = 16 marks

END OF SECTION TOTAL FOR SECTION A = 64 MARKS

SECTION B

Answer ALL questions. Write your answers in the spaces provided.

5 Analyse the effectiveness of Piaget's schematic development theory in supporting the cognitive development of a 3-year-old in an early years setting.

12 marks

If asked to **analyse**, consider how to break down the theme, topic or situation to explore the interrelationship of different aspects.

To show your skills in response to a long-answer question, consider how to:
- **demonstrate accurate** and thorough knowledge
- **apply knowledge** to the context of the question
- **structure and balance** your answer by showing competing viewpoints
- **use specialist language** consistently and fluently
- provide a **supported conclusion**.

At the age of 3, children are still learning by using all their senses so they need to be given plenty of opportunity for hands-on experiences. Piaget's schematic development theory explains this process whereby children construct meaning through their play activity. He saw this as a learning cycle. He suggested that children develop concepts as they play, which are referred to as schemas. If children's experiences fit with their schema they are in a state of equilibrium.

Write two or three sentences suggesting why practitioners should regularly update and change play activities and resources, making links to Piaget's state of disequilibrium and how this leads to the development of new schemas (equilibrium).

....

....

....

....

....

....

....

Write two sentences about the importance of planning for support and providing a balance of child-initiated and adult-led activities. Make links to criticisms of Piaget and theories that focus on how adult support for learning can promote children's thinking skills.

....

....

....

....

....

Reach a conclusion as to the extent of Piaget's influence in the design of the early years curriculum, which requires a balance of child-initiated and adult-led activity.

....

....

....

....

....

....

....

Links Look at page 19 of the Revision Guide to revise Piaget's schematic development theory.

Total for Question 5 = 12 marks

6 Evaluate the importance of the key person role in an early years setting with reference to theories of development.

14 marks

To answer this '**Evaluate**' question, you could consider:
- relevance or significance, e.g., of a theory, factor or life event
- strengths and weaknesses
- advantages and disadvantages.

> **Guided** >

✎ **It is useful to plan your answer using a spider diagram.**

Role: knows the child well; carries out observations; security; relationships with parent; supports transition

Bowlby: importance of a main carer; builds relationship; secure bond important for learning

Relevance / Significance

Bronfenbrenner: mesosystem and importance of interaction between home and nursery

Maslow's hierarchy of needs: getting to know the child, and being able to meet basic individual needs

....

....

....

....

....

....

....

....

....

....

....

....

....

....

....

....

....

....

....
....
....
....
....
....
....
....
....
....
....
....
....
....
....
....
....
....
....
....
....
....
....
....

> **Links** To revise the theories, look at page 10 of the Revision Guide for Maslow, page 31 for Bronfenbrenner and page 32 for Bowlby and Ainsworth.

Total for Question 6 = 14 marks

END OF REVISION PAPER
TOTAL FOR SECTION B = 26 MARKS
TOTAL FOR PAPER = 90 MARKS

Revision paper 2

To support your revision, this Workbook contains revision questions to help you revise the skills that might be needed in your exam. The details of the actual exam may change so always make sure you are up to date. Ask your tutor or check the Pearson website for the most up-to-date Sample Assessment Material.

SECTION A

Answer ALL questions. Write your answers in the spaces provided.

Some questions must be answered with a cross in a box ☒. If you change your mind about an answer, put a line through the box ☒ and then mark your new answer with a cross ☒.

---

1   Milek and Ania have two children:
- Aron aged 3 years
- Josep aged 6 years.

The family lives in a small tenth-floor flat. They have no family living nearby. Milek works as a security guard but only earns a basic wage. Ania is unable to get a job.

Josep is developing his reading and numeracy skills at school but finds writing difficult. Aron stays at home with Ania during the day and has formed a strong attachment. The health visitor is concerned that Ania has become isolated and has helped her to find a place for Aron at a local Children's Centre.

(a)   Which aspect of Josep's fine motor skills is expected at 6 years?   `1 mark`

- ☐ **A**   Can draw a simple figure with head, body and limbs
- ☐ **B**   Can copy circle shapes and lines
- ☐ **C**   Can draw a detailed figure adding hair and eyes
- ☐ **D**   Can use palmar grasp to make marks on paper

(b)   List **three** ways that poverty and isolation may impact on Aron's physical development.   `3 marks`

1 ....

....

2 ....

....

3 ....

....

(c)   Describe **two** ways that going to nursery will help to promote Aron's social and emotional skills.   `4 marks`

1 ....

....

....

....

2 ....

....

....

....

(d) Use Bowlby's theory of attachment to discuss the importance of Aron building a strong attachment with his mother.

8 marks

....

....

....

....

....

....

....

....

....

....

....

....

....

....

....

....

Links Look at pages 28 and 29 of the Revision Guide to revise emotional and social development, and page 32 for Bowlby's theory of attachment.

Total for Question 1 = 16 marks

2 Saira has three children:
- Saeed, who is 8 months old
- Alesha, who is 2½ years old
- Naseem, who is 4 years old.

Saira now lives alone with her children as her husband left the home after their marriage broke down three months ago. She works part time so Alesha and Saeed go to a local nursery each morning. Naseem is in the reception class at school.

Saeed can now sit unaided and rolls over to reach toys. Alesha enjoys nursery and has a special friend who she likes to play with. Naseem's teacher has told Saira that he has become withdrawn at school and is reluctant to play with other children.

(a) Identify **two** milestones for Alesha's language development that she would be expected to achieve when she reaches 3 years.

2 marks

1 ....

....

2 ....

....

(b) Give **two** examples of ways that practitioners can support Naseem to deal with his emotions.

2 marks

1 ....

....

....

2 ....

....

....

(c) Describe **two** ways that understanding the principles of growth and development can help practitioners to support Saeed.

4 marks

1 ....

....

....

....

2 ....

....

....

....

(d) Discuss the possible effects of the family breakdown on Naseem's emotional development.

8 marks

....

....

....

....

....

....

....

....

....

....

....

....

....

....

....

....

Links Look at pages 1 and 2 of the Revision Guide to revise principles of growth and development, page 28 for emotional development, and page 37 for the possible effects of transition on emotional development.

Total for Question 2 = 16 marks

3 Madie is a childminder. She cares for Erin, aged 2 years, for three days each week, and Connor, aged 6 years, after school each day.

Madie provides lots of materials and activities such as treasure baskets, sand play and art activities that keep Erin busy each day. Erin enjoys playing alongside Connor when he gets home from school. Recently Connor got frustrated when building a model and kicked it down. The next day Madie noticed Erin kicking down a tower she had made from blocks.

Connor likes to be active so Madie often takes the children to the park on the way home from school, where Connor can play football, use the swings and climb.

(a) Which theory best helps to explain Erin's behaviour with the blocks? `1 mark`

☐ **A** Bowlby's theory of attachment
☐ **B** Bandura's social learning theory
☐ **C** Piaget's schematic development theory
☐ **D** Bruner's three modes of cognitive representation

(b) Give **three** examples of language development that Erin should have achieved at her age.

`3 marks`

1 ....

....

....

2 ....

....

....

3 ....

....

....

(c) Explain **two** ways that going to the park can support Connor's physical development. `4 marks`

1 ....

....

....

....

2 ....

....

....

....

(d) Discuss why early play and learning experiences are important for Erin's neurological development.

8 marks

....

....

....

....

....

....

....

....

....

....

....

....

....

....

....

Links Look at pages 9 and 13 of the Revision Guide to revise aspects of physical development, page 5 for neurological development and page 16 for language development.

Total for Question 3 = 16 marks

4 | Pearl is 3½ years old. She goes to her local nursery school.

Each day, Pearl is encouraged to take part in a range of play activities that support cognitive development, including construction play, sand and water play, 2D and 3D shapes, pattern making and weighing.

Pearl also loves to take part in role play, particularly the role-play shop where she likes to dress up as the 'shopkeeper' and make up a storyline. Pearl tends to lead the play and often finds it difficult to share toys. She sometimes snatches them and then a practitioner has to intervene.

(a) List **two** activities that could promote Pearl's problem-solving skills.

2 marks

1 ....

....

2 ....

....

(b) Give **two** examples of how practitioners can help Pearl to understand the emotions and feelings of others.

2 marks

1 ....

....

2 ....

....

(c) Describe **two** ways that information processing theory can be used to support Pearl's cognitive development.

4 marks

1 ....

....

....

....

2 ....

....

....

....

(d) Discuss how Piaget's universal stages of development help to explain Pearl's involvement in role play.

8 marks

....

....

....

....

....

....

....

....

....

....

....

....

....

....

....

....

Links Look at page 20 of the Revision Guide to revise Piaget's stages, page 21 for information processing, and page 26 for mathematical concepts/cognitive development.

Total for Question 4 = 16 marks

END OF SECTION TOTAL FOR SECTION A = 64 MARKS

SECTION B

Answer ALL questions. Write your answers in the spaces provided.

5   Analyse the effectiveness of guided participation with adults and peers in the development of mathematical concepts of a child aged 4 years in an early years setting. Make reference to Vygotsky's Zone of Actual/Proximal Development.

12 marks

You may need more space to complete your answers to questions worth 12 or 14 marks.

If so, you should continue your answer on a separate sheet.

....

....

....

....

....

....

....

....

....

....

....

....

....

....

....

....

....

....

....

....

....

Total for Question 5 = 12 marks

6 Evaluate how theories of behaviour can help to explain a 3-year-old's social and emotional development in an early years setting.

14 marks

....

....

....

....

....

....

....

....

....

....

....

....

....

....

....

....

....

....

....

....

....

....

....

Links Look at page 17 of the Revision Guide to revise Vygotsky's Zone of Proximal Development and page 30 for theories of behaviour.

Total for Question 6 = 14 marks

END OF REVISION PAPER

TOTAL FOR SECTION B = 26 MARKS
TOTAL FOR PAPER = 90 MARKS

Unit 2: Development of Children's Communication, Literacy and Numeracy Skills

Your set task

Unit 2 will be assessed through a task, which will be set by Pearson. You will need to use your understanding of how children develop literacy, language, numeracy, mathematical and communication skills and how to promote and support this development. You will respond to fictional case studies of an early years setting and one or more learners from early years settings. You will then complete activities based on these case studies.

Your Revision Workbook

> This Workbook is designed to **revise skills** that might be needed in your assessed task. The details of the actual assessed task may change so always make sure you are up to date. Ask your tutor or check the **Pearson website** for the most up-to-date **Sample Assessment Material** to get an indication of the structure of your assessed task and what this requires of you.

To support your revision, this Workbook contains a revision task to help you revise the skills that might be needed in your assessed task. The revision task is divided into sections.

Reading the task and making notes

In your Workbook you will use your skills to:

- Read a task brief to get a picture of the setting, play and learning environment, age groups of the children and types of backgrounds and needs of the children.
- Read case studies that provide further information, such as:
  - issues relating to the setting
  - the stage and development needs of a child who attends the setting
  - the stage and development needs of a child or group of children with any developmental delay or needs they may have.
- Structure relevant notes that relate the activities in the task to the information in the case studies and your own knowledge, involving:
  - making and justifying recommendations in response to the issues relating to the setting
  - producing a set of actions in response to the stage and development needs of a child who attends the setting
  - designing activities to address any developmental delay or needs children may have.

Responding to the activities

Your response to the activities will demonstrate your knowledge and understanding about the development of literacy, language, numeracy, mathematical and communication skills in relation to the realistic situations and contexts in these case studies and the associated activities.

> **Links** To help you revise skills that might be needed in your Unit 2 exam, this Workbook contains a revision task starting on page 25. See the introduction on page iii for more information on features included to help you revise.

Reading the task brief

To support your revision, this Workbook contains a revision task to help you revise the skills that might be needed in your assessed task. The details of the actual assessed task may change so always make sure you are up to date. Ask your tutor or check the Pearson website for the most up-to-date Sample Assessment Material.

Read the task brief thoroughly to get a picture of the setting. This will give you an overview of the:
- play and learning environment
- age groups of children you will need to take into account
- types of additional needs you may need to address
- family background of the children, including those whose home language is not English.

East Hill School

East Hill School has a Foundation Stage Department for children aged 3 years up to 5 years, a nursery for children aged 3 to 4 years and a reception class for children who reach 4 years by 1 September up to those aged 5 years. It is located in a small market town. There are a number of Eastern European families living in the area who do not speak English at home. Four reception children and two nursery children have additional language needs.

East Hill has separate nursery and reception rooms, and has recently acquired a shared outdoor area, which they hope to develop as an additional play and learning area. There are currently 20 children in the reception class and 24 children in the nursery. Twelve of the nursery children attend mornings only.

Activity 1

Read the case study carefully. Case studies allow you to demonstrate your knowledge and understanding about:
- key features and stages of development
- theories that help to explain development
- different approaches and their impact on the promotion of skills
- activities and resources to support the skills
- ways to provide support for children whose home language is not English and those with additional needs.

East Hill and improvements required in literacy skills

Assessment at 11 years has shown that children progressing to secondary school from East Hill School are weak in literacy skills compared to children from other primary schools in the area. The headteacher believes that improvements must start at Foundation Stage. What the Foundation Stage Department needs to do to improve is:
- *maximise opportunities for literacy development, indoors and outdoors, to include children with additional learning needs and those with a home language that is not English*
- *promote children's skills and abilities in reading and writing through daily adult-led activity*
- *extend the use of theoretical approaches to reading across the staff team.*

Produce a report responding to the headteacher's request in response to concerns about literacy development. You must:
- make recommendations to the Foundation Stage Leader
- describe the resources required
- describe the role of early years educators and parents
- justify improvements that link best practice to early years theory.

Activity 1 – Making notes

Read and understand the task and case study

Guided
 Start your planning and notes for Activity 1 by making sure that you understand the task brief and the case study on page 25. Outline the type of setting and age groups of the children that are the basis for the task. The information can form part of the **introduction** to your report.

The setting and age groups of children

• The setting is part of a .... and organised into two

   separate areas: a nursery for children aged .... and a

   reception class for children aged ....

• East Hill School has:
   – a group of 20 children who are between 4 and 5 years
   – a group of 24 nursery children, half of which attend mornings only
   – children in the nursery and reception class who have additional language needs
   – children whose home language is not English.

The reason for producing my report

• The purpose of my report is to make recommendations on ways to ....

   and describe resources that will ....

• The report must show how improvements link to best practice and ....

   ....

The audience for my report

• ....

Additional learning needs, language needs or other considerations to consider when writing my report

....

....

....

....

Structure and focus your notes

Identify **topic areas** for making notes that you would find useful when writing your **report** for Activity 1. For example, complete the notes below, looking for links between the brief and the case study when making recommendations for maximising literacy experiences.

<u>Maximise opportunities for literacy development, indoors and outdoors, for children aged 3 years to 5 years to include children with additional learning needs and those with a home language that is not English</u>

- Ideas for play and learning activities and environment to support <u>writing</u> skills indoors and outdoors, and the resources needed.

- Ideas for play and learning activities and environment to support <u>reading</u> skills indoors and outdoors, and the resources needed

<u>Promote children's skills and abilities in reading and writing through daily adult-led activity</u>

- Share books and rhymes.

- ....

- ....

<u>Extend the use of theoretical approaches to reading across the staff team</u>

- ....

- ....

- ....

Make notes on literacy development and promoting reading and writing skills

> **Guided**

 The first two points made in the case study are about what the Foundation Stage Department needs to do to improve.

1 Maximise opportunities for **literacy development**, indoors and outdoors, to include children with additional learning needs and those with a home language that is not English.

2 Promote children's skills and abilities in **reading and writing** through daily adult-led activity.

To do this, make notes on ways that the early years educators can build a language-rich environment.

1 Maximise opportunities for literacy development, indoors and outdoors, to include children with additional learning needs and those with a home language that is not English

• Staff should make sure that resources accessible to children are clearly labelled with a picture and word(s). There should be areas that are designated for reading and writing activities where

children have a choice of materials. Displays must be ....

....

....

• Six play activities that can support children in developing their reading and writing skills and abilities, to include activities for an outdoor setting.

• Role play post office

• ....

• ....

• ....

• ....

• ....

• Resources needed that can support the identified play activities.

....

....

2 Promote children's skills and abilities in reading and writing through daily adult-led activity

• Three ways that staff can engage with children to promote reading and writing skills as they play.

• ....

• ....

• ....

• Advice to parents – three ways of supporting reading and writing skills at home.

• ....

• ....

• ....

> **Links** To revise characteristics of a language-rich environment, look at page 63 of the Revision Guide. For ideas for activities that support literacy activities, look at pages 66, 73, 75, and to revise ways that adults can support, look at page 62, 65, 69, 70, 71, 73 and 86.

Make notes on extending use of theoretical approaches

Guided

 The third and final point made in the case study about what the Foundation Stage Department needs to do to improve is as follows.

3 Extend the use of **theoretical approaches to reading** across the staff team.

To do this, start by outlining three theoretical approaches that early years educators may use to support children's reading skills in the context of the setting. Remember to give the advantages and disadvantages of each, referring to best practice and how they lead to improved outcomes.

3 <u>Extend the use of theoretical approaches to reading across the staff team</u>

• The synthetic phonics approach supports children's understanding of phonemes (sounds) and graphemes (written letters). They are taught individually to enable children to segment words.

....

....

• ....

....

....

• ....

....

....

Links To revise theoretical approaches, look at page 67 of the Revision Guide.

Make notes on theorists and theories

Guided

 Now identify three theorists and their theories that help to explain how the environment, provision and adult engagement support best practice.

• Vygotsky – social constructivism and how children can be supported to reach the next stage of

development (Zone of Proximal Development) ....

....

....

• ....

....

....

• ....

....

Links To revise theorists and how they support literacy skills, see pages 54–56, for report writing and justifying recommendations see pages 92–93, and for relating to theories, see page 97.

Activity 1 – Making and justifying recommendations

Using preparatory notes

In this Workbook you can refer to any of the notes you have made as you respond to the activities.

In your actual assessment, you may not be able to refer to notes, or there may be restrictions on the length and types of notes that you can take into your supervised assessment. Check with your tutor or look at the most up-to-date Sample Assessment Material on the Pearson website for more information.

Use the information from the brief and case study for Activity 1 (page 25) and your revision notes to make and justify recommendations in a **formal report**. In your report you must:
- make recommendations to the foundation stage leader
- describe the resources that are required, including the role of early years educators and parents
- justify improvements that link best practice to early years theory.

Use the space below to write your report, using the guidance and headings to help you.

Guided

 Start by creating a plan before your write your report. This helps ensure that your information is well-structured and your ideas flow logically.

In your report, include:
- an **introduction**
- the body of the report, with **recommendations** and **reasons to justify them**, including:
  - a language-rich environment with indoor and outdoor play and learning activities to support literacy and reading and writing skills and abilities for children between 3 and 5 years
  - how children's reading and writing skills can be promoted through adult-led activity and engagement, including advice that can be given to parents
  - theoretical approaches used by early years educators to support and promote reading skills and abilities
- a **conclusion** justifying recommendations 0with reference to best practice and relevant early years theories.

Plan for my report

Report

This report has been produced by ....

and is intended for ....

....

> State your own name as the author of the report, and that it is intended for the Foundation Stage Leader.

Introduction

The purpose of this report is to make recommendations for improvements

to the ....

.... the Foundation Stage Department, East Hill School.

> Introduce the purpose of the report, then complete the recommendations that follow.

Recommendations for a language-rich environment

The nursery and reception class must be organised to capture children's

interest and curiosity about reading and writing. This can be achieved by

....

....

....

....

There should be designated areas ....

....

....

....

....

Recommendations for activities that promote literacy, and required resources

It is recommended that children have opportunities to take part in the following play activities to

promote their reading and writing skills.

Role play should always be available. It should be changed regularly to include home, shop play and

health clinic. These give opportunities for ....

....

....

Art activities, including collage (cutting and sticking) and painting, must always be available to

promote fine motor skills that are essential for ....

....

....

Story time should be part of the daily routine. ....

....

....

Table-top games and puzzles should be provided each day to ....

....

....

Sand play should be provided, indoors and outdoors, to ....

....

....

Computer programmes will support reading skills because ....

....

....

Resources and materials must be easily accessible to support activities. They should include ....

....

....

The role of early years educators and parents to promote improvement in skills

> Explore ways that adults (practitioners and parents) can support children in the activities identified to develop early reading and writing skills.

Staff should engage with children in their role play and imaginative play. For example, ...

....

....

....

....

....

....

Parents can be advised on ways to support literacy at home by ....

....

....

....

Theoretical approaches

....

....

....

....

> Recommend ways to extend the use of theoretical approaches to reading across the staff team.

....

....

....

....

Conclusion

....

....

....

....

....

....

....

....

....

....

....

....

....

....

> Refer back to the purpose of your report and fully justify your recommendations with explicit links to early years theories.

Activity 2

> *Jakub is 3 years old and has just joined the nursery class.*
>
> *His parents recently moved to the UK from Poland. His father can speak some English but his mother speaks none so the family always use Polish in the home. His father works, so Jakub is brought and collected from the nursery by his mother.*
>
> *Jakub has been assessed in his home language, which shows that he has well-developed communication skills and is meeting his expected milestones in other areas of his development.*
>
> *He tends to sit alone and is reluctant to join in games with other children. He enjoys art activities, painting, drawing, and cutting and sticking.*
>
> *One of the lunchtime supervisors working at the school speaks Polish.*
>
> Produce a set of actions that can support Jakub and his family.
>
> You must:
> - suggest actions that exemplify best practice
> - describe the resources required
> - describe the role of the early years educator and parents
> - justify your actions with reference to early years theory.

Activity 2 – Making notes

Read and understand the task and case study

   Start your planning and notes for **Activity 2** by making sure that you understand the case study and what is required of you. Read the case study carefully to ensure you understand the context of Jakub and his family's needs. Consider the importance of recognising and supporting a child in their home language while learning the language of the setting. The focus here is on Jakub's **speech**, **language** and **communication**. It is important that you recognise the difference between speech and language, and literacy skills.

List six key pieces of **information** about Jakub and his family that will help you to identify a set of actions.

Information about Jakub and his family to help me identify a set of actions

- Jakub can communicate confidently in his home language

- Jakub only hears Polish spoken at home

- ....

- ....

- ....

- ....

Make notes to identify topic areas

Guided Next, make notes to produce **a set of actions** that can support Jakub and his family.

Start by identifying six **topic areas** for making notes that you would find useful to produce a set of actions for Activity 2.

Topic areas for producing a set of actions that can support Jakub and his family

- The role of the key person

- Stages of second language development

- ....

- ....

- ....

- ....

Make notes to identify realistic goals

Guided Now refer again to the case study for Activity 2. Identify four **realistic goals** that adults should work towards to support Jakub in his development of English.

Four realistic goals that adults should work toward to support Jakub in his development of English

- For Jakub to be able to understand and follow the routines at nursery

- ....

- ....

- ....

Make notes that suggest actions

Guided Next, suggest some **actions** that can support Jakub to work towards each of the identified goals.

One or two actions that can support Jakub to work towards each of the identified goals

- Display a visual timetable. Share the timetable with Jakub's parents.

- ....

 Links To revise identifying goals and effective actions, look at pages 83 and 84 of the Revision Guide.

Make notes on resources and the role of the adult

> Guided

 Now, for each action you must identify appropriate **resources** that will support it. You should also identify the **role of the adult** to show how the actions should be delivered and/or supported.

Resources needed to support the actions suggested

- A visual timetable showing the key events of the day, to include, lunchtime, story time, home time, etc.

....

....

....

....

The role of the early years educator and Jakub's parents in supporting actions

The early years educator should:

- Point to the visual image on the timetable to help Jakub to make links between the words and events, e.g. snack time and sitting on the carpet and sharing fruit.

....

....

Jakub's parents should:

- ....

....

....

> Read between the lines in the case study – there is a hint about ways to support Jakub. A member of staff speaks Polish, so how could they help with supporting Jakub and his family?

> Guided

 Identify appropriate **resources** and the **role of adults** in supporting it.

- ....

....

....

....

....

....

....

- ....

....

....

....

....

....

Make notes on links with early years theory

Next, outline three **early years theories** to explore **best practice** in supporting the development of second language skills and abilities.

<u>Three early years theories to explore best practice in supporting the development of second language skills and abilities</u>

• Vygotsky emphasised the importance of social interaction for language development. This can be with adults or children who have skills in what is being learned.

• ....

....

• ....

....

Links Look at pages 54, 55 and 84 of the Revision Guide for the importance of social interaction in the learning process and theories that support this approach. Consider the key person role and the importance of this for Jakub. Look at page 83 for the stages of second language acquisition that help to explain Jakub's stage, and how knowing this can help adults to understand the level of support he requires. To revise sets of actions, see pages 94–95 of the Revision Guide.

Activity 2 – Producing a set of actions

Using the information from the case study for Activity 2 (page 34) and your revision notes, produce your set of actions.

You must:
- suggest actions that exemplify best practice
- describe the resources required
- describe the role of the early years educator and parents
- justify your actions with reference to early years theory.

> **Guided** >

 A set of actions consists of a **breakdown of experiences** that can be used to support Jakub's skills and abilities. Actions must be unambiguous and specific.

You must include:
- **the purpose/introduction**
- **realistic goals**
- **actions that will support** Jakub toward the identified actions
- how actions will be supported, including **resources** and the **role of adults**
- a **conclusion** to justify the choice of actions with links to theories that help to explain best practice.

You could start by creating a plan, then write your set of actions below using the guidance and headings to help you.

Background

Jakub is 3 years old. He is proficient in his home language. He has just joined the nursery and has no understanding of English. He speaks Polish with his family at home.

Introduction

The purpose of this set of actions is to ....

....

....

....

....

> Think carefully about your introduction. Outline the purpose of the actions, including the goals that Jakub is working towards. Being clear about your aims will help you to develop a set of coherent actions.

Set of actions

....

....

....

....

....

....

....

> You can organise your information in the way you think best. If using the separate headings provided here, make sure that you clearly link the resources and the role of the adult to the relevant action. Another approach you could take is to identify resources and the role of the adult immediately following each identified action.

....

....

....

....

....

....

....

....

....

....

....

Resources to support actions

....

....

....

....

....

....

....

....

....

....

....

....

....

....

....

....

....

Adult role

....

....

....

....

> This should include responsibilities and ways the adult will engage with Jakub, including early years educators and parents. Actions should be clearly linked to roles.

....

....

....

....

....

....

....

....

....

Conclusion

....

....

....

> Look back at the case study and set of actions to make sure you have made explicit links to early years theory.

....

....

....

....

....

....

....

....

....

Activity 3

Design **two** activities for children who are in the **reception class** to promote their understanding and use of measurement. The activities must consider the needs of a child with **hearing loss** and two children with **language delay**. You must consider the contribution and support made by the early years educator.

Produce a plan for each activity, including:
- information about the resources required
- the role of the early years educator, adults and others
- how the activity can meet the needs of the individual children
- justification for your actions by linking best practice to early years theories.

Activity 3 – Making notes

Read and understand the task and activities you need to design

> Start your planning and notes for Activity 3 by making sure that you understand what is required of you. Read the brief for Activity 3 carefully. Although this requires you to plan for children's understanding and use of **measurement**, you must take into consideration their **needs** (including hearing loss; language delay).
>
> Identify six topic areas for making notes that you would find useful to produce a plan for each of the two activities for Activity 3.

Topic areas that are useful for producing a plan of each activity

- An outline for an activity plan

- Ideas for measurement activities with links to curriculum objectives

- ....

- ....

- ....

- ....

Make notes to identify headings you will need in each activity plan

> Next, identify each **type of information** that you will need to include in each activity plan.
>
> Complete the spider diagram below.

Age group

Activity plan

Resources

 To revise the required content for an activity plan, look at page 96 of the Revision Guide.

Make notes to identify learning goals

  List what the children must learn about measurement (**learning goals**) linked to their age/stage of development and the Foundation curriculum requirements.

Measuring can involve activities that give practice in:
- length/distance
- weighing
- time
- capacity.

What children must learn about measurements (learning goals)

- Ordering objects according to their length

- Using balance scales to identify objects that weigh more or less than a given object

- ....

- ....

- ....

- ....

- ....

Make notes that suggest two activities

  Use information about what children should learn about measurement (learning goals) and suggest **two activities** that will support children to work towards them. Include terms linked to the activity.

When selecting your activities, choose different types of activity. This will enable you to demonstrate different aspects of your knowledge, skills and abilities. You might plan one activity that is **child-initiated** and one that is **adult-led**, for example, showing how the adult role may differ. It is important that you identify **mathematical terms** relevant to your activity and use these consistently; for example, heavier than, lighter than, full, empty.

Two activities to support children working towards learning goals about measurement, with linked terms

Activity 1

....

....

....

Mathematical terms ....

....

....

Activity 2

....

....

....

Mathematical terms ....

....

....

Make notes on roles and individual needs

  Note four ways that the **early years educator**, **adults** or **others** can support each activity, along with **individual support** for children with additional and language needs (hearing loss; language delay).

Four ways that the early years educator, adults or others can support each activity

- Asking open-ended questions to promote thinking

- ....

- ....

- ....

Individual support for children with hearing loss and language delay

- For children who have language delay, the adult should make sure they have eye contact. Speech

  should be ....

  ....

- For children with hearing loss, the adult should make sure the child is sitting facing them.

  The adult should also use ....

  ....

Links Look at pages 78–81 of the Revision Guide to revise ideas on how to support children in numeracy and mathematical skills, and page 86 for ways to support children with additional language needs.

Make notes on links with early years theories

Theories that focus on how children learn will be helpful in **explaining activities** that support children's cognitive development in their understanding of measurement. You should also consider **how theorists explain** the importance of engagement with children to help them to progress.

Identify three theorists and their theories that can help to justify the practice you describe in your activities to support children's learning.

Three theorists and their theories that can help to justify the practice described in the activities to support children's learning

- Piaget – links to activities that provide opportunities for 'hands-on' measuring activities that enable children to construct their understanding.

- ....

  ....

- ....

  ....

Links Look at pages 54, 55 and 56 of the Revision Guide to revise relevant early years theories, pages 94 and 96 to revise activity plans and page 97 for relating to theories.

Activity 3 – Producing two activities

Use the information from the brief for Activity 3 (page 41) and your revision notes to design two activities for children who are in the reception class to promote their understanding and use of measurement, considering the needs of a child with hearing loss and two children with language delay. Consider the contribution and support made by the early years educator.

You must produce a plan for each activity, including:
- information about the resources required
- the role of the early years educator, adults and others
- how the activity can meet the needs of the individual children
- justifying your actions by linking best practice to early years theories.

For **Activity Plan 1**, headings have been provided to help you. For **Activity plan 2,** you need to provide headings yourself.

Start by producing a **plan for your activities**. This will ensure that your activity plans are well structured and your ideas flow logically. Refer to your notes and include:
- the **age/stage** of the children
- information on **additional needs** of individual children
- what children need to learn (**learning goals**)
- a **detailed breakdown** of each activity
- **resources** and **adult engagement** that support each of the activities
- a **conclusion** justifying your activity plans, with reference to best practice and relevant early years theories.

Use the space below to plan your two activities before starting to write.

Plans for activities

Guided › ACTIVITY PLAN 1

Age and group ....

Additional needs

This activity takes into account the needs of ....

....

....

Learning goals

By taking part in this activity children will ....

....

....

....

> Make sure that your learning goals are relevant to the age and stage of the children and requirements of the Foundation curriculum.

Description of activity

....

....

....

....

....

> Consider how you will conclude the activity. Think of ways you can get children to reflect on their learning and construct their understanding. How might this be explained by Piaget's constructivist learning theory?

....

....

....

....

....

Resources

....

....

....

> You should provide some detail to include where the activity will take place, types of resources, materials, equipment and their use.

....

....

....

....

....

....

Role of the adult

....

....

....

> Include ways that the adult can introduce mathematical terms during the activity.

....

....

....

....

....

....

....

Justification for activity plan

....

....

....

....

....

....

....

....

....

....

....

....

....

....

....

....

....

....

....

ACTIVITY PLAN 2

For your second activity plan, consider how you will use the space provided, and include your own headings.

....

....

....

....

....

....

....

....

....

....

....

....

....

....

....

....

....

....

....

....

....

....

....

....

....

....

ACTIVITY PLAN 2

....

....

....

....

....

....

....

....

....

....

....

....

....

....

....

....

....

....

....

....

....

....

....

....

....

....

END OF REVISION TASK

Unit 4: Enquiries into Current Research in Early Years Practice

Your set task

Unit 4 will be assessed through a task, which will be set by Pearson. You will be given a current piece of research into early years and asked to carry out your own secondary research related to the issue. You will need to use your understanding of the methodologies of contemporary research, apply your knowledge of early years educational issues, and investigate the implications for early years practice. You then respond to activities based on the research.

Your Revision Workbook

> This Workbook is designed to **revise the skills** that will be needed in your assessed task.
>
> The details of your actual assessed task may change from year to year so always make sure you are up to date. Ask your tutor or check the **Pearson website** for the most up-to-date **Sample Assessment Material** to get an idea of the structure of your assessed task and what this requires of you.

To support your revision, this Workbook contains a revision task to help you revise the skills that might be needed in your assessed task. The revision task is divided into sections.

1 Research

In your Workbook you will use your skills to:
- read and make notes on a provided research article covering an aspect of recent research (pages 50–61)
- carry out your own independent secondary research using at least two secondary sources related to the issue in the research article and make notes (pages 62–74)
- prepare a list of your secondary sources (page 75).

2 Activities

Your response to the activities will help you to revise:
- understanding of research methods and the validity and reliability of results in research (page 78)
- understanding of the **relationship** between **your own secondary research** and a **provided article,** and how this relationship reinforces the **importance of the issue** (page 80)
- **planning** and **ethical** considerations for **further research** (page 83)
- **research implications** for **future provision** and/or **practice** (page 86).

> **Links** To help you revise the skills for your Unit 4 set task this Workbook contains a revision task starting on page 77. See the introduction on page iii for more information on features included to help you revise.

Revision task

To support your revision, this Workbook contains revision tasks to help you revise the skills that might be needed in your set task. The details of the actual task may change so always make sure you are up to date. Ask your tutor or check the Pearson website for the most up-to-date Sample Assessment Material.

This Workbook provides the article 'Childcare Sufficiency and Sustainability in Disadvantaged Areas' to demonstrate one way that you can:

- analyse an article, carry out secondary research based on the content of the article and make notes
- use your research to respond to four activities.

The reference for this article is: Dickens, S., Wollny, I. and Ireland, E. (2012) 'Childcare Sufficiency and Sustainability in Disadvantaged Areas' [Online] Available: www.gov.uk/government/uploads/system/uploads/attachment_data/file/219621/DFE-RB246.pdf [22 April 2016].

In your actual set task the choice and focus of research pieces will vary each year. An example given on the Pearson website is an extract from the article 'Sustained Shared Thinking in an Early Childhood Setting: an Exploration of Practitioner's Perspectives' (2014).

1 Research

Plan and monitor your research

  When carrying out research you need to break it into stages. Estimate how long you will need for each part, then plan and monitor your time to ensure you can complete everything you need within the time allocated. The stages involved in research in this Workbook are noted below.

Stages of research

1	Read and annotate the article
2	Familiarise with the article, making notes and identifying issues
3	Note key words on the content of the article, in order to search for secondary research sources
4	Search and note possible sources for secondary research, based on the content of the article
5	Assess reliability of secondary source 1, chosen with reference to Source, Appearance, Methods, Timeliness, Applicability and Balance (SAMTAB), ethical considerations, and important areas of research
6	Make focused bullet notes on secondary research source 1, including a focus on methods, reliability, ethics, importance of issue, further research (e.g. proposal, timing, ethics), impact of research on practice and provision. Show the links in relationship to the provided article
7	Assess reliability of secondary source 2 using the approach outlined in 5 above.
8	Make focused bullet notes on secondary source 2 using the approach outlined in 6 above

Read and annotate the article

Pages 51–75 of this Workbook demonstrate how you can analyse a provided article, carry out your own secondary research, and make notes. This is based on the article 'Childcare Sufficiency and Sustainability in Disadvantaged Areas' below.

Read the article and the annotations. You could add your own, to highlight and summarise the issues. Then complete the notes under 'Familiarise yourself with the article' starting on page 58. Use the notes and analysis provided to guide you.

Guided

Childcare Sufficiency and Sustainability in Disadvantaged Areas

Published September 2012, Department for Education

Introduction and background

Childcare providers in disadvantaged areas are more susceptible to financial difficulties, because of fewer parents using childcare. As a result they are more financially vulnerable than providers in other more affluent areas. Childcare providers in disadvantaged areas face challenges in terms of remaining sustainable and improving quality (Ofsted Annual Report, 2009/10).

As part of the Fairness Premium announced by the coalition government, from September 2013, the least advantaged two-year-olds will be entitled to 15 hours of free early education. For this policy to be successful there will need to be enough places available. The purpose of this project was to:

- explore how successful local authorities feel that they have been in securing the sustainability of childcare places in disadvantaged areas
- examine the challenges local authorities and childcare providers face in providing sustainable childcare and what factors explain sustainable provision of places or otherwise
- explore if more support is needed for local authorities to ensure there are enough places for two-year-olds for the roll out of free hours from 2013.

Key findings

This research has found that sustainable childcare provision in disadvantaged areas needs to be publicly funded in one form or another. In those areas where a free market model of childcare operated, there were enough childcare places to meet parental demand, but these places were threatened by the financially difficult situations many of the providers felt they were in.

Quality was higher in the disadvantaged areas **where the local authority subsidised and directed the shape of provision**. For PVI providers, maintaining quality was both costly and risky. Key concerns, associated with quality improvement mentioned by all providers included: the removal of free training, paying for and retaining better qualified staff and paying for staff time to complete paperwork associated with training.

Local authority childcare planning in disadvantaged areas was focused on increasing the capacity of group-based providers and childminders, increasing the sustainability of PVI providers and improving the quality of childcare provision.

Providers in disadvantaged areas were heavily reliant on providing funded places as demand for paid for places was low. Core running costs had increased and providers were often struggling to keep their fees low and remain flexible. Financial sustainability was affected by

Annotations:

Reputable source – gives study validity.

Purpose of research and importance of issue.

Aims of the researchers.

The key findings – link to my own secondary research.

The researchers have gathered and linked information from LAs and providers. Private, voluntary and independent providers are affected by different factors, often reliant on fee paying parents.

Could lead to introduction of new statutory training requirements/higher skilled staff.

the extent to which providers were able to attract better-off fee paying families, whether local populations were transient, local attitudes towards the use of formal care, the accessibility of the setting, the extent of local competition, rent costs and the business skills of individual providers. Whilst providers were reliant on the funding for two-, three- and four-year-olds' places, not all felt that it was adequate to cover their costs.

Whilst there was considerable support and enthusiasm for the roll out of the two-year-old entitlement among local authorities and childcare providers, they strongly felt that it will not be possible to achieve enough high quality places through market forces alone. The reasons for this varied across the different types of providers involved in the case study areas:

- Private providers did not think it would be financially worthwhile to deliver places for disadvantaged two year olds under the roll out.
- Voluntary and independent sector providers and local authority-funded providers will need capital funding to expand or adapt their premises.
- Voluntary and independent sector providers will also need considerable support to deliver the entitlement, for example, revenue funding to cover gaps between the extension of premises and the filling of places, funding for workforce development and funding to allow them to increase staff ratios.
- Childminders in these areas may respond to market demand to a certain extent but many parents in disadvantaged areas perceive childminders as a less attractive option than group-based care.[1]
- Childminders were also concerned that involvement in the two-year-old entitlement will lead to an increase in what they already regard as an onerous level of paperwork.

Method

The study looked at ten local authorities and used a case study approach. The project involved:

- analysing local authority Childcare Sufficiency Assessments
- a literature review of parental demand for and knowledge about childcare in disadvantaged areas
- interviews with local authority strategists
- interviews with up to five group-based pre-school providers (such as children's centres, and private, voluntary and independent sector nurseries, day care and sessional care providers) and two childminders in each local authority.

Interviews with local authority strategists and childcare providers were carried out between March and May 2012. The research findings presented here are based on this evidence, and should not be generalised to other local authority areas.

Main findings

Models of childcare provision in disadvantaged areas

Four different models of childcare provision in disadvantaged areas were identified. Under Model 1, a range of provider types were operating self-sufficiently in the market, with no local authority-funding. Model 2 providers also operated self-sufficiently, with the occasional exception of sustainability funding from the local authority. In Models 3 and 4, there was a strong history and presence of local authority subsidised and run provision. In the case of Model 3 this formed the bulk of the available provision, in Model 4 local authority-run provision was complemented by local authority funded voluntary sector provision. In Models 1 and 2 there was a lot of choice for parents because of the range of provider types operating and because there was spare capacity. There was also choice in Model 4 and spare capacity in the voluntary sector provision. Some providers in the

---

Four different models of childcare provision researched.

Fees would be charged at a higher rate than 2-year-old funding. Costs higher, e.g. for more staff.

Implications for staff training and career development. Also, may lose money by being flexible because places are not being filled full time.

If true of all settings, this would impact on job role.

Main methods: analysis of LA assessments, interviews with strategists and providers. Relied on literature review of parental demand for places, not interviews to find their views. This could have implications for findings/ opportunities for further research.

Different 'models' of provision are identified depending on the level of government funding received. Ranges from Model 1 being settings that are self-sufficient and rely on parents paying fees to Model 4 which includes authority run and funded settings. Makes the research more robust.

PVI sector in Models 1 and 2 and voluntary sector in Model 4 were struggling financially because of low demand for day care, childcare funding being insufficient to cover increasing overheads and maintain quality and competition between each other and the maintained sector. In Model 3 parental choice was more limited and providers carried few vacancies. The subsidised providers in Models 3 and 4 whilst more financially sustainable were dependent on future public funding.

Provision planning

> Supporting evidence on the importance of funding.

Local authorities were carrying out a range of activities and planning in relation to pre-school provision in disadvantaged areas. These included:

- **Increasing the capacity for group-based funded places** for the two-year-old roll out and increasing three- and four-year-olds' places in areas with increasing birth rates.

> This point reinforces the importance of the study.

- **Helping the financial sustainability of PVI providers** by providing business support and support to improve quality. There was particular concern about the financial situation of PVI providers because of increases in childcare costs and changes to the childcare element of the Working Tax Credit.

> This point links to evidence from interviews with providers.

- **Increasing childminder capacity** by recruiting new childminders and providing training to improve the skills of new and existing childminders.

- **Improving knowledge about and access to childcare to increase demand** by providing information to parents about childcare costs, three- and four-year-olds' places and early education; by working with employers, childcare providers, Jobcentre Plus, community advice services, minority ethnic groups, health visitors, social care and parent support agencies.

> This point links to the literature review on parents/demands/needs.

- **Improving the quality of childcare** by assessing all providers against local authority quality standards and giving support to lower quality providers from higher quality providers, link teachers and specialist childcare consultants. Support and access to training had, however, been cut in some areas.

The local authorities in our study were also working **to improve how they measure whether there are sufficient childcare places locally and improve access to childcare for children with Special Education needs or a Disability (SEND) a**cross the whole authority, in both disadvantaged and non-disadvantaged areas.

> Possible issue for further research.

Financial sustainability of providers

Local authority strategists and childcare providers interviewed felt that the financial stability and sustainability of childcare providers was affected by a range of different interrelated factors.

> Interviewing LA strategists and providers – triangulation method that gives validity to results.

- **Economic factors.** A key overarching factor was that in many areas the cost of day care was felt to be too expensive for many local parents, which left providers reliant on providing funded places. This was exacerbated for many by the increasing costs of providing childcare alongside the perceived need to keep fees low to attract parents.

- **Central government policies.** The current two-, three- and four-year-old funding played a pivotal role in the financial sustainability of providers. While some relied on it to stay in business, the extent to which the funding level covered their costs depended on their experience of local and provider level factors discussed below. The childcare element of the Working Tax Credit had helped to create demand for childcare among low income parents in disadvantaged areas, but providers had already started to feel the effects of the changes to it through parents reducing the amount of childcare they used. Quality standards required by central government (such as those needed for the Early Years Foundation Stage) were seen as being costly as they resulted in additional training, having to pay better quality staff higher salaries and additional paperwork. Providers with high Ofsted ratings found it helped their financial situation as it attracted parents. ◄———

> Settings will need to strive to improve Ofsted ratings to attract parents.

- **Local area characteristics.** Important local area characteristics which could also have a strong impact on providers' financial sustainability were: the extent to which a local area contained a transient population, which could cause fluctuating levels of demands for childcare; the cost of property, which was often higher in urban areas, resulting in higher outgoings for providers; whether a provider had to pay full rent for their premises; the extent to which travel costs posed a barrier to access for local families (a particular problem in rural areas); cultural and attitudinal barriers ◄— to using childcare in the local community which could result in lower parental demand for childcare; the extent to which a provider was able to attract more affluent families, which depended on where they were situated; and whether a provider was experiencing competition from other local childcare providers or the maintained nursery sector.

> Providers need to gain a higher profile/improve quality to attract more parents so they are more financially secure.

- **Provider level factors.** Important factors here were whether providers were able to attract better-off fee paying parents, or benefited from low rent or other charitable contributions such as donations of time or resources. The business skills of providers ◄— in terms of the ability to forward plan, be flexible and creative, fundraise and effectively use marketing tools were also seen as influential factors in relation to financial sustainability.

> Implications for training to include an element of business and marketing for those progressing to management/ ownership of early years provision.

- **Local authority approach.** The extent to which the local authority subsidised childcare was crucial to the sustainability of childcare providers. In Models 1 and 2, (a free market model with limited local authority involvement), some providers were concerned about their financial sustainability due to their negative experiences of the factors listed above. In Models 3 and 4 where the local authority subsidised day care and wraparound care, these funded providers were more financially secure. However, local authority intervention in the free market models remained key. Business advice, support with safeguarding and quality issues and sustainability funding were highly valued by providers and seen as critical to their survival. ◄—

> Building relationship with local authority important for providers.

Parents' perspective

Evidence from the case study areas, analysis of Childcare Sufficiency Assessments and relevant literature explored why parents in disadvantaged areas might perceive that there is not enough childcare ◄— available even though providers in these areas are often operating with vacancies.

> Explains triangulation of evidence from LAs analysis and interviews, providers interviews and literature review around parents' needs.

- **Sufficiency of childcare places in disadvantaged areas.** The evidence from the analysis of Childcare Sufficiency Assessments suggests that families living in disadvantaged areas and who want day care may in some cases find it difficult to find a place. This was particularly the case if they needed flexible childcare, childcare for atypical hours,[2] or childcare for children with SEND.[3] However, providers in our study felt that demand was not high enough for them to be able to fill vacancies.

- **Perceptions about childcare.** Evidence from the literature also ◄— showed that the perceptions of childcare amongst parents, who were facing multiple or different forms of disadvantage, could inform their views about what was available locally:

> Evidence of parents' perceptions less current than feedback from LAs and providers. Opportunity for further research.

  - **The role of information.** Parents in disadvantaged areas were more likely to say they did not have information about childcare and relied more on word of mouth, than those in more advantaged areas.[4] ◄—

> Is this still true if LAs have been providing more information about childcare provision?

  - **Perceptions of suitability of childcare.** Strong cultural and attitudinal barriers narrowed the choices available to some parents in these areas, for example, preferences for group-based nursery care over childminders and perceptions about what sort of care is 'for them'.[5]

- **Perceptions about the quality of childcare.** Parents in disadvantaged areas were more likely to have concerns about the quality of childcare provision than better-off families.[6]
- **Cost of childcare.** There is strong evidence from our research and from the literature that the cost of childcare was a key barrier to parents facing disadvantage,[7] particularly for parents of children with SEND.[8] However, there was also evidence that the perception of childcare as unaffordable may occur in part because of a lack of information about the actual cost.[9]

Is this true or a perception? Raises more questions about training and staffing.

Roll out of the two-year-old entitlement

There was great willingness among providers to take two-year-olds under the roll out. A lot of preparation for the roll out was also already underway among local authorities.

The roll out was seen by providers as being very beneficial to two-year-olds and their families as it could improve children's outcomes and provide important parenting support for families and could help them back into employment. Some providers also felt it gave them opportunities to fill vacancies, secure a more reliable source of income and raise quality standards.

Supports other research that suggests children can benefit from pre-school experience – purpose of research study.

Both providers and local authority strategists had some concerns and thought there would be challenges with the roll out, due to the short timescale for the roll out and uncertainty about how it might work in practice.

Roll out of the two-year-old entitlement – concerns and challenges for providers

- One of the main concerns for providers was that the **level of funding** for the entitlement would not be enough to meet the additional needs of children and families (such as speech and language needs, parenting support), extra administrative demands (such as attending multi-agency meetings, arranging specialist support) or the rising salary costs of providing quality childcare.
- Another concern was that there would not be a **level playing field** for different types of providers to be involved because of local authority policies that prioritised some types of providers over others.
- Some providers were also concerned about how to deal with **high numbers of eligible children** and that they may have to turn away other children in favour of funded two-year-olds.

Implications for staff role.

Roll out of the two-year-old entitlement – concerns and challenges for local authorities

Further research opportunities.

A key concern for local authorities was how to raise the **quality standards** in sufficient numbers of childcare settings to provide enough places. They were also concerned that there were not enough qualified staff available to work with two-year-olds, and were unsure how training and workforce development to improve quality standards could be funded.

Another issue for local authorities was how to **develop systems to identify and monitor eligible children.** Local authority strategists and providers also felt that **broader income-based eligibility criteria** may mean that some children miss out on the places, such as children of low income working parents and children with SEND.

A lack of support services such as family support and speech and language therapists was an issue in some local authorities. There was also a concern that **cultural and attitudinal barriers** to using formal childcare would make it difficult to encourage parents to take up the entitlement in certain areas within local authorities.

Capacity for the roll out

In areas operating under the free market model (Models 1 and 2) there was some capacity to take funded two-year-olds. This was mostly in the voluntary and independent sector that had vacancies or could convert vacant baby or three- and four-year-olds' places to be suitable for two-year-olds. There was also some capacity under Model 4, within the voluntary sector. However, across all the models the vacancies that were available would not be sufficient to be able to meet the numbers needed for the roll out. There was less capacity in Model 3, because the local authority-funded settings were full and PVI sector provision was limited.

> Draws a conclusion about capacity relating to types of provision.

Support needs to ensure sufficient capacity for the roll out

The providers and local authority strategists interviewed identified a number of support needs necessary to ensure there will be sufficient capacity for the roll out.

- **Capital funding to expand or adapt premises** of local authority-funded providers in Models 3 and 4 and voluntary and independent sector providers in Models 1, 2 and 4.
- **Revenue funding** for voluntary and independent sector providers and childminders to keep places open until they could be filled by two year olds.
- **Funding for workforce development** to bring enough staff up to the qualification levels required to deliver the entitlement and to equip them with the skills to work with younger children, many of whom, providers felt from their experience of the current two-year-old initiative, may have additional needs.
- **Funding to allow providers to increase staff ratios** needed for working with two-year-olds and to deal with the additional meetings, and paperwork requirements anticipated under the roll out.
- **Clarity and better information on the specifics of the roll out** which had not been provided when the fieldwork was taking place, on exactly which two-year-olds would be eligible, what quality standards will be required, what funding will be available and what support there will be for local authorities to prepare.

> These points summarise the implications for provision of the roll out of free education to 2-year-olds, e.g. without additional funding places may not be kept open and there may not be sufficient experienced and qualified staff.

Conclusion

This research has found that whilst providers and local authority strategists were generally very supportive of the roll out of the two-year-olds' entitlement, they did not feel that it would be achievable without additional funding to create the requisite extra places and to raise quality standards.

> Conclusion – briefly draws together evidence to show that unless funding is in place, provision is not sufficient or sustainable.

DFE-RB246, ISBN 978-1-78105-152-8 September 2012

Sarah Dickens, Ivonne Wollny and Eleanor Ireland

References

[1]Vincent, C., Ball, S. and Braun, A. (2008) *Local childcare cultures: Working class families and pre-school childcare*. London: Institute of Education/ESRC.

Roberts, J. (2011) 'Trust and early years childcare: parents' relationships with private, state and third sector providers in England', *Journal of Social Policy*, 40 (4), pp. 695-715.

Andrew Irving Associates (2008) *Promoting Take-up of Formal Childcare Among Low Income Families: Message testing research*. Research Report RR068: Department for Children, Schools and Families.

> Journal – possible source of secondary research.

> Literature review – recognised sources/information from expert in the field – evidence of parents' perceptions based on this. Possible implications as views of parents will have been sought before changes in Government policy on extending free childcare to 2-year-olds. Opportunity for future research.

[2]Singler, R. (2011) *Open all hours? Flexible childcare in the 24/7 era.* Daycare Trust.

[3]Cheshire, H., Brown, V., and Wollny, I. (2011) *Impact evaluation of the Disabled Children's Access to Childcare pilot (DCATCH)*, Research Report DFE-RR168. Department for Education.

Speight, S., Smith, R., Lloyd, E. (2010) *Families experiencing multiple disadvantage: their use of and views on childcare provision.* Research Report DCSF-RR191: Department for Education.

Green, E. and Knight, G. (2007) *Evaluation of the Childcare Taster Pilot and Extended Schools Childcare Pilot Programmes: Further Qualitative Research into Implementation.* Research Report SSu/2007/FR/026: Department for Children, Schools and Families.

[4]Speight et al (2010) op cit.

[5]Vincent et al (2008) op cit.

Roberts (2011) op cit.

Irving Associates (2008) op cit.

[6]Speight et al (2010) op cit.

[7]OPM (2008) *Reviewing Childcare Sufficiency Assessments.* Department for Children, Schools and Families.

Smith, R,. Poole, E., Perry, J., Wollny, I., Reeves, A. and Bryson, C. (2010) *Childcare and Early Years Survey of Parents 2009.* Research Report DFE-RR054: Department for Education.

Speight et al (2010) op cit.

[8]KIDS (2011) *Are Cuts to Local Authority Budgets Denying Families the Right to Childcare?* London: KIDS

[9]Speight et al (2010) op cit.

Daycare Trust – possible organisation for secondary research.

DfE reports may be a good starting point for secondary research.

Familiarise yourself with the article

 As you read the article, analyse it and make focused bullet notes.

Complete the notes below for the article on pages 51–57. The six questions can be used to structure notes on any research piece. Some notes have been started for you, with one person's response to the article. Refer to the article and notes, and add your own thoughts below.

Notes on article: Dickens, S., Wollny, I. and Ireland, E. (2012) 'Childcare Sufficiency and Sustainability in disadvantaged areas'. [Online] Available: www.gov.uk/government/uploads/system/uploads/attachment_data/file/219621/DFE-RB246.pdf [22 April 2016].

1 <u>What was the research piece about and why was it important?</u>

 Complete the bullet notes as you consider **the purpose** in finding out the current state of provision and **why** it needs to be not only sustained but increased to meet demands. Why was the research issue considered **important** and what could it **result** in?

- timing and subject of study was important because from 2013 free pre-school provision, already in place for three to four year olds, was due to extend to disadvantaged two year olds
- free provision introduced because previous research showed that quality provision can reduce gap in attainment between disadvantaged children and others of the same age by the time they start school
- research was carried out in order to understand local authority strategy relating to early years provision
- researchers wanted to understand how local authorities ....

....

....

....

....

....

....

....

....

2 <u>What were the key methods used in the research and how did they support reliable outcomes?</u>

 The notes below should **identify** and **explain** the **qualitative methods** and **case study** approach so a reader can understand them. When looking at methods used in research, remember that some articles may not say whether the methods are qualitative, quantitative or mixed. Remember: numbers and charts are likely to be quantitative; words, language and speech are likely to be qualitative. Numbers/charts/words/language may be mixed methods.

Complete the bullet notes below with a comment on **reliability**. To do this, use the notes around the article and think about triangulation of methods by looking from the perspective of local authorities and providers.

- study used qualitative methods, appropriate where strategy and opinions are being sought
- case study approach was used based on the experiences of different types of provision across ten local authorities
- local authority (LA) sufficiency assessments were analysed and LA strategists were interviewed
- literature review looked at the level of demand, needs and perceptions of parents in disadvantaged areas

- interviews were carried out with different types of pre-school providers within each of the LAs.
- different models of provision were identified depending on the level of government funding received.
- these ranged from Model 1, being settings that are self-sufficient and rely on parents paying fees, to Model 4, which included authority run, authority-funded and supported settings.
- triangulation of different methods led to reliable outcomes, through ....

....

....

....

....

3 <u>What were the key findings in the research?</u>

Guided

✎ Complete the notes below to identify and explain the key findings in the research.

Researchers reached five key conclusions from their research:

1 Provision in disadvantaged areas: ....

....

2 In disadvantaged areas where providers were subsidised and supported by the LA, provision was

shown to be ....

3 The strategy of local authorities focused on ....

....

4 Providers in disadvantaged areas were reliant on funding for several reasons including: ....

....

....

....

5 Providers were supportive of the policy to extend free childcare to disadvantaged 2-year-olds but believed it was not possible to offer the quality of childcare that was required if they had to rely on market forces. Reasons given were different across the different types of childcare.

   - Private providers ....

   - Voluntary and independent providers ....

   ....

   - Childminders..

   ....

   - Parents ....

   ....

- There was commitment to supporting policy to roll out free education to 2-year-olds but there were factors impacting on the financial stability and sustainability of providers.

4 <u>Were any recommendations/future research plans discussed?</u>

 Guided

> ✏️ Although no specific research plans were discussed in the study the notes should correctly identify possibilities relating to the issues. Some of the factors that affect financial security of providers, could be possible research issues. The notes should highlight the ways that researchers could investigate parents' perceptions.
>
> Complete the notes to give a brief **example** of a useful piece of future research. Bear in mind **ethical considerations** and timelines. Using **tentative language** such as 'could' and 'might', and 'suggests', is appropriate in a research context.

- although the study does not give specific recommendations it highlights concerns and challenges
- concerns raised about sufficiency and quality of places indicate further research may be needed on ability of providers to meet possible additional parental support, and communication, language and care needs of the children
- ten local authorities provided a substantial sample although researchers felt they could not generalise evidence across other LAs
- when interviewed, strategists and providers were in agreement that sustainability of provision was affected by a number of different factors such as running costs, management skills, accessibility
- any or all of these issues could also lead to further research.
- parents' perceptions were not sought through interview or questionnaire, as with other key stakeholders, instead relying on a literature review, meaning that views in relation to the new policy of free education for 2-year-olds were not taken into account
- the literature review found that parents in disadvantaged areas felt they had less information about childcare than those in advantaged areas (Speight 2010, as cited in Dickens, Wollny and Ireland, 2012)
- local authorities planned to improve information to parents so a useful piece of future research might be to

....

....

....

....

....

> Although the ethical considerations in the research are not mentioned, because it was based on local authorities and funded and supported by the DfE it is likely that ethical methods were used. Researchers interviewed providers and LA strategists and did not involve children in their research which would have involved additional safeguarding considerations and permissions.

5 <u>What could be the implications/impact on practice?</u>

 Guided

> ✏️ Continue the notes below on being prepared for **change** and the **implications** for pay and security of employment. You could suggest additional **training** to support the needs of disadvantaged 2-year-olds and their families, use of **best practice** to attract parents and **funding**, and **developing skills** in management, managing costs, securing funding and marketing.

- research findings for this study help providers to be aware of issues that could impact on their setting if taking on 2-year-olds

- implications for my own practice ....

....

....

....

6 <u>What could the implications/impact be on early years provision?</u>

 Make bullet notes below. You could:
- note how the four different models of provision can be clearly **addressed** using targeted **funding** and **support** with marketing of the setting
- comment on how the roll out of pre-school provision to disadvantaged children and families could mean greater inclusion, leading to **improved outcomes** for children and families
- consider how earlier identification of needs can **result in improvement** in the development and well-being of children, reducing later specialist interventions and **saving time** and **costs** to professional early years services.

....

....

....

....

....

....

....

 Links The Revision Guide revises ways of approaching the research process.
- Pages 98–102 revise the purposes, issues, rationale and planning for research.
- Pages 103–113 revise research methods, ethical issues and confidentiality.
- Pages 114–124 revise research skills including notes, records and referencing techniques, and searching for and selecting appropriate secondary sources.
- Pages 125–130 revise evaluation of research, including bias and interpretation in research.
- Pages 131–134 revise future research, and recommendations/implications for practice and provision.

Note key words for searching for secondary sources

  Next, you need to identify at least **two** secondary research sources based on the content of the provided article, and make notes. The bibliography and source for the article are good places to start.

You could use simple **internet key word searches** such as 'two-year-olds', 'disadvantaged families', 'early years funding'. You can also use Boolean operators in your search. For example: **'and'** brings up all terms you type in, such as childcare providers and funding; **'or'** brings up either childcare providers or funding; **'not'** brings up childcare providers not funding. If you use ***** after a word it, will bring up all possible extensions. For instance, 'partner *' will bring up 'partnership', 'partners'.

Using the bibliography contained in the article (ages 56–57), note four possible key words you could use for an internet search for secondary sources. Two have been suggested for you.

<u>Key words for an internet search for secondary sources, based on the provided article</u>

1 take-up of free early years education

2 costs <u>and</u> childcare

3 ....

4 ....

Search and note possible sources

When searching for sources you need to refine your search from many possibilities to at least two. It is important to include the considerations below.

- Links with the issues of research in the provided article.
- If your sources include different research methods, you can show the ways they are effective to research the issue, their use of data, and how they have been chosen to support reliable outcomes.
- The importance of the issue for research, and ways the source includes future research considerations and the impact of research on provision and practice.
- The reliability and validity of the source, using criteria to check against (e.g. SAMTAB, pages 65–66).

You could search on the website of the source of the article (DfE) and other organisations involved in early years research. It is good practice to make a note of key information on possible sources for reference as shown below, along with some key points to remind you of the research.

Choose at least two of the four key words noted on page 61 to search the internet and note possible sources. Narrow these down to at least two secondary research sources that best relate to the content of the provided article and the considerations above. Use the format below and create any additional records you need.

Title of research piece or article: ....

Name(s) of author(s): ....

Source of article (e.g. journal, web page, government site): ....

Year of publication: .... Page numbers, if applicable: .... If web page, date accessed: ....

URL: ....

Some key points: what the research was about, methods, findings, links to provided article:

....

....

....

....

Title of research piece or article: ....

Name(s) of author(s): ....

Source of article (e.g. journal, web page, government site): ....

Year of publication: .... Page numbers, if applicable: .... If web page, date accessed: ....

URL: ....

Some key points: what the research was about, methods, findings, links to provided article:

....

....

....

....

Title of research piece or article: ....

Name(s) of author(s): ....

Source of article (e.g. journal, web page, government site): ....

Year of publication: .... Page numbers, if applicable: .... If web page, date accessed: ....

URL: ....

Some key points: what the research was about, methods, findings, links to provided article:

....

....

....

....

Title of research piece or article: ....

Name(s) of author(s): ....

Source of article (e.g. journal, web page, government site): ....

Year of publication: .... Page numbers, if applicable: .... If web page, date accessed: ....

URL: ....

Some key points: what the research was about, methods, findings, links to provided article:

....

....

....

....

Title of research piece or article: ....

Name(s) of author(s): ....

Source of article (e.g. journal, web page, government site): ....

Year of publication: .... Page numbers, if applicable: .... If web page, date accessed: ....

URL: ....

Some key points: what the research was about, methods, findings, links to provided article:

....

....

....

....

Links To revise searching for sources, see pages 121–124 of the Revision Guide.

> The choice of secondary research source 1 in this Workbook is noted below.

Guided

Notes on secondary research source 1

Title of research piece or article: Gibb, J. et al (2011) 'Rolling out free early education for disadvantaged two year olds: an implementation study for local authorities and providers' [Online] Available: www.gov.uk/government/uploads/system/uploads/attachment_data/file/181502/DFE-RR131.pdf [28 April 2016]

Some key points: what the research was about, methods, findings, links to provided article:

The roll out of free education to disadvantaged 2-year-olds; approaches to ensuring sustainable provision; greater focus on identifying eligible families and improving quality and flexibility of provision; uses qualitative data. Relates to content in provided article.

> Complete details for secondary source 2 underneath, with one of your chosen secondary research sources from pages 62–63.

Notes on secondary research source 2

Title of research piece or article: ....

Name(s) of author(s): ....

Source of article (e.g. journal, web page, government site): ....

....

Year of publication: .... Page numbers, if applicable: .... If web page, date accessed: ....

URL: ....

Some key points: what the research was about, methods, findings, links to provided article:

....

....

....

....

....

....

....

Complete a SAMTAB on secondary research source 1

 You need to identify whether the secondary research you would like to use comes from a reputable source as this will give you an indication as to whether it can be relied upon. You can assess the validity and reliability by completing a SAMTAB for the **S**ource, **A**ppearance, **M**ethods, **T**imeliness, **A**pplicability and **B**alance of the secondary sources you consider.

- The SAMTAB below shows you the kinds of things you can record, using secondary research source 1 as an example. Make sure you also take account of any ethical considerations.

- The SAMTAB will help you to assess how secondary research sources meet the criteria you need, so you proceed with at least two sources that are most suitable.

There is no requirement for you to use a SAMTAB in your actual set task unless it is of use to you.

Read the guidance and entries that follow on secondary research source 1. You can use some of the information to help complete the notes on pages 67-70.

Assessing reliability and validity of a research source –
Source, **A**ppearance, **M**ethods, **T**imeliness, **A**pplicability, **B**alance (**SAMTAB**)

RESEARCH TITLE AUTHOR SOURCE	Use a referencing format (e.g. Harvard)
	Gibb, J. et al (2011) 'Rolling out free early education for disadvantaged two year olds: an implementation study for local authorities and providers' [Online] Available: www.gov.uk/government/uploads/system/uploads/attachment_data/file/181502/DFE-RR131.pdf [28 April 2016]
SOURCE	Does it come from a reputable source/ journal (usually noted on the web page)? Is author information included? Do you know the publisher? Note that Wikipedia may not always be a reliable source.
	The information comes from the Department for Education, which is responsible for education and children's services in England. Government sources are reliably accurate and may also be informed by government policy.
APPEARANCE	Can you read and understand it? Does it look professionally written (e.g. correct spelling and grammar)? Some sources may not necessarily be reliable as you may not know the credentials of the author.
	The information in the article is clear and there is a good summary at the beginning that highlights the main points of the study. It is professionally written with no grammatical or other errors. The layout and appearance look professionally prepared.

METHODS	Does it use appropriate methods for the study? Are the methods clear? How big is the study? Do the research methods support reliability of results? Is the method similar to the provided article, or different?
	It examines the government programme to roll out free education to all disadvantaged 2-year-olds. It uses a case study approach similar to the provided article to explore the issue from the perspective of local authorities, key stakeholders and providers. The methods and size supported reliability of results in targeted areas.
TIMELINESS	Is it up to date? It is best practice to find up-to-date material, e.g. the past ten years. Anything older may not be so reliable as society, thinking and research changes. Some old sources retain relevance – e.g. Piaget's cognitive theories of the 1960s.
	This article was published in 2011 and is therefore up to date. It would be possible to research recent data for numbers of 2-year-olds receiving free education to see how local authorities and childcare providers are continuing to manage the provision that has been rolled out.
APPLICABILITY	Does it focus on the issues/questions you are exploring? Research may be interesting but not necessarily relevant to the area being explored. If so, it will not add value. How does it link with your provided article?
	Yes. Improving the quality of provision for disadvantaged children and their families is an important issue if children are to be as ready for school as advantaged children of the same age. Secondary research source 1 supports findings about the availability, financial sustainability and quality of early years provision. The research includes information that links with the provided article.
BALANCE	Does it give a non-judgemental view? Does the author adopt a particular standpoint? If the author gives opinions that are not backed up by research, they may be showing bias to an issue, instead of substantiated fact.
	Yes. This article is authentic and based on case study evidence to illustrate how local authorities were managing the roll out. It used in-depth questioning to gather data from local authority staff, different types of childcare providers and other stakeholders. It drew on evidence from 44 staff across 8 LAs: 16 group settings, 11 childminders and 4 childminding coordinators. Therefore there is a good level of validity.

Links Page 124 of the Revision Guide supports using a SAMTAB and ethical checklist.

Make notes on secondary research source 1

> **Guided**

 You need to make focused bullet notes on the research sources you choose. They should be objective and report what is written in the article. Using a computer can be a good way to organise your notes.

Read the following notes on secondary research source 1, and the guidance in the tinted boxes. Then use information from these notes and the SAMTAB on pages 65–66 to complete the notes towards the end.

Notes on secondary research source 1: Gibb, J. et al (2011) 'Rolling out free early education for disadvantaged two year olds: an implementation study for local authorities and providers' [Online] Available: www.gov.uk/government/uploads/system/uploads/attachment_data/file/197682/DFE-RB131.pdf [28 April 2016]

1 <u>What was the research piece about and why was it important?</u>

The notes below give a good overview of the study. It is good practice to **summarise research** so you gain a good understanding of what the study was **about** and how it might be relevant to the provided article. The notes should identify a useful **link** between secondary research source 1 and the provided article.

- study commissioned by the Department for Children, Schools and Families (now the DfE) and carried out by researchers from National Children's Bureau (NCB) and National Centre for Social Research (NatCen)
- roll out of free early years education to 2-year-olds aimed to improve outcomes for disadvantaged children and reduce developmental gap between them and other children by the time they start school
- report aimed to identify progress made in extending free education using case studies of eight local authorities, and the providers and stakeholders within each LA area
- report recognises that rolling out additional places can bring pressures on providers who may be inexperienced in supporting 2-year-olds and/or families with complex needs
- report cites concern regarding additional time and funding needed as the offer is scaled up.
- links well with the provided article as it cites issues around the number and quality of places, funding and ensuring quality of provision

2 <u>What were the key methods used in the research and how did they support reliable outcomes?</u>

The notes below identify that the research was based on **qualitative methods**. They should also identify how **limitations** in the number and type of group settings could make the findings less **reliable** than a larger sample.

- methods used were qualitative, as appropriate for understanding factors and reasons behind strategies
- research is based on case studies from information gathered from local authorities, and staff and other stakeholders responsible for early years provision
- views and perceptions of parents not sought and might have supported findings about availability of quality provision
- urban and rural local authorities, of different sizes took part, including most disadvantaged and advantaged areas, giving a representative overview of strategies and experiences
- however, only 16 group care settings were involved, which is an average of two in each LA, making the findings less reliable than if a larger sample had been used across more types of setting
- in addition, 11 childminders were interviewed
- researchers found that the expertise of LAs to track the impact of roll out differed so it may have affected the reliability of information gathered

 Links Pages 125–130 of the Revision Guide revise interpreting and presenting data.

3 What were the key findings in the research?

> The numbered headings below show the **issues** identified, and the **findings** are drawn together under them. There is a final summary of some **key findings** of the study.

1 Identifying eligible families:

- evidence showed that the knowledge of professionals such as health visitors was critical to engage with families who could be eligible for free places
- children's centres were seen as important as they coordinated family support
- conclusion was reached that, in addition, a record of children coming up to 2 years should be available

2 Funding:

- local authorities were committed to ensuring that any provision they funded was of high quality, but it was recognised that as the offer was rolled out providers with less experience would need to be involved, who would require further support in the form of training and resources
- researchers identified difficulties faced by LAs for balancing the needs of the family, the best provision for the child and financial viability of providers

3 Quality:

- it was found that Ofsted ratings may not be the best indicators, and local and national schemes were used to measure quality
- questions were raised regarding what quality was acceptable

4 Summary of key findings:

- there was commitment across local authorities, providers and stakeholders to roll out the offer, but with flexibility in allocating funding depending on local conditions
- however, as the number of providers needs to be increased to accommodate increased numbers, there may be those who are not equipped or sufficiently experienced to deal with the more complex needs of disadvantaged 2-year-olds and their families
- there were also questions around the quality level of provision that would be acceptable and how this would be assessed as the offer was rolled out

4 Were any recommendations/future research plans discussed?

Guided

> Complete the bullet notes below to briefly consider a future research plan, including:
> - **Types of method and reliability:** Consider sample size and availability of information to collect and analyse further data for reliable findings.
> - **Relationship to the provided article:** Building on the link identified, you could plan research on how to investigate the training needs of providers using the framework of the four models identified in the provided article.
> - **Limitations in current research to address in future research:** You could consider limitations relating to parents' perspectives and measures for provision that meets quality requirements.
> - **Planning:** Take into account ethical considerations such as informed consent and data protection; research skills required (those you have and those you need). To help inform this, you could research into Ofsted and local authority quality assessment strategies, training opportunities and the most recent data on 2-year-olds in pre-school.
> - **Research literature:** You could note any recognised sources/information from experts in the field which would link well with the article and future research.

- researchers suggest that although local knowledge by professionals was effective in identifying eligible families, birth data should be used
- relating to quality, it was shown that additional training is required by providers who do not have experience in supporting disadvantaged children and families
- researchers found a lack of guidelines to level the acceptable quality of provision
- shown that market conditions can vary so LAs needed to be flexible in applying funding

• further research could consider issues around quality and training needs, which were highlighted to address the lack of provider's experience in some areas

....

....

....

....

....

....

....

....

....

....

....

....

....

....

....

....

....

....

....

....

....

Links For more on future research, see page 133 of the Revision Guide.

5 What could be the implications/impact on practice?

 Use notes in this section and the SAMTAB (pages 65–66) to complete bullet notes on how the roll out to 2-years-olds can impact on the setting and individual practice.

As with the provided article, you could look at issues around **training needs** to be able to **support** more complex needs of disadvantaged children and their families. You could look at **skills required** to engage and support children and their families and how to **respond** to their **needs**.

You could also look at **different types of provision** and give reasons why local authorities relied on children's centres to play a key role.

....

....

....

....

....

....

....

....

6 What could the implications/impact be on early years provision?

> Use notes in this section and the SAMTAB (pages 65–66) to complete bullet notes on how local authorities can **identify** and **engage** eligible 2-year-olds and their families to ensure that their needs are being met. This may mean becoming more **flexible** to meet parents' needs as well as the children's.
>
> As with the provided article, you could consider the factors that can impact on **financial sustainability**. You could explore the role of the local authority to provide **training** and **support**, and how **funding** might be available to ensure minimum **quality standards**.

....

....

....

....

....

....

....

....

....

....

....

....

Links Pages 131–132 of the Revision Guide revise recommendations for practice and provision.

Complete a SAMTAB and notes on secondary research source 2

 Using your chosen secondary research source 2, noted on page 62, assess validity and reliability by completing a SAMTAB for the **S**ource, **A**ppearance, **M**ethods, **T**imeliness, **A**pplicability and **B**alance. Consider ethical principles also. Use the example of the SAMTAB on secondary research source 1 (pages 65–66) as a guide. Make sure you move forward with a suitable source 2.

Assessing reliability and validity for secondary research source 2	
ARTICLE TITLE AUTHOR SOURCE	Use a referencing format (e.g. Harvard) ....
SOURCE	Does it come from a reputable source/journal (usually noted on the web page)? Is author information included? Do you know the publisher? Note that Wikipedia may not always be a reliable source. ....
APPEARANCE	Can you read and understand it? Does it look professionally written (e.g. correct spelling and grammar)? Some sources may not necessarily be reliable as you may not know the credentials of the author. ....
METHODS	Does it use appropriate methods for the study? Are the methods clear? How big is the study? Do the research methods support reliability of results? Is the method similar to the provided article, or different? ....

TIMELINESS	Is it up to date? It is best practice to find up-to-date material, e.g. the past ten years. Anything older may not be so reliable as society, thinking and research changes. Some old sources retain relevance – e.g. Piaget's cognitive theories of the 1960s.
	....
APPLICABILITY	Does it focus on the issues/questions you are exploring? Research may be interesting but not necessarily relevant to the area being explored. If so, it will not add value. How does it link with your provided article?
	....
BALANCE	Does it give a non-judgmental view? Does the author adopt a particular standpoint? If the author gives opinions that are not backed up by research, they may be showing bias to an issue, instead of substantiated fact.
	....

Now complete bullet notes on your chosen secondary source 2. Use the examples and comments on the article (pages 51–61) and secondary source 1 (65–70) to guide you.

Notes on secondary source 2: ....

1 <u>What was the research piece about? (E.g. what it explored, why important, what the study looked at to find out.)</u>

....

....

....

....

....

....

....

....

2 <u>What were the key methods used in the research? (E.g. qualitative, quantitative, mixed; how they supported reliability of research.)</u>

....

....

....

....

....

....

....

....

3 <u>What were the key findings in the research? (E.g. What were the results of the study. Did they answer the research questions? What were the conclusions of the research?)</u>

....

....

....

....

....

....

....

4 Were any recommendations/future research plans discussed? (E.g. Do they recommend further research? Were there any aspects of the research that did not go well? Consider proposal, methods, reliability, research skills required, ethical considerations, timescales.)

....

....

....

....

....

....

....

5 What could be the implications/impact on practice? (E.g. How can this type of research affect individuals in the workplace? How will it affect individual practice?)

....

....

....

....

....

....

....

....

6 What could the implications/impact be on early years provision? (E.g. What are the wider implications on society and the cost and effectiveness of early years providers?)

....

....

....

....

....

....

....

....

List your sources

 When carrying out research you need to list your secondary research sources. Complete the list below with the sources used in the Workbook, using a recognised reference system such as Harvard.

Secondary source 1:

Gibb, J. et al (2011) 'Rolling out free early education for disadvantaged two year olds: an implementation study for local authorities and providers' [online] Available: www.gov.uk/government/uploads/system/uploads/attachment_data/file/181502/DFE-RR131.pdf [28 April 2016]

Secondary source 2 (note the reference for your secondary source listed on page 62):

....

....

....

....

....

Using preparatory notes

In this revision Workbook you can refer to any of the notes you have made as you respond to the activities.

In your actual assessment, you may not be able to refer to notes, or there may be restictions on the length and type of notes that you can take into your supervised assessment. Check with your tutor or look at the most up-to-date Sample Assessment Material on the Pearson website for more information.

Links Notes for the article start on page 51, secondary source 1 on page 64, secondary source 2 on page 71.

2 Revision activities

To respond to the revision activities you will have carried out research on the following:
- the provided article: 'Childcare Sufficiency and Sustainability in Disadvantaged Areas'
- secondary research source 1: 'Rolling out free early education for disadvantaged two year olds: an implementation study for local authorities and providers'
- secondary research source 2: Your chosen researched secondary source.

In your actual assessment:
- the provided research piece will be new each year and the secondary research source will relate to it
- you may able to use your preparatory notes, or there may be restrictions on the length and type of preparatory notes you can use. Check with your tutor or look at the latest Sample Assessment Material on the Pearson website for more information.

Provide a reference list of the sources you have used in addition to the article

List your secondary sources here, using a recognised referencing system (e.g. Harvard). When giving research sources:
- list them in alphabetical order. If two references start with the same name, list them in date order, with the most recent date first
- where an acronym is used, cite the full name and the acronym in brackets the first time used. You can then just use the acronym, e.g; Department for Education (DfE).

....

....

....

....

....

....

....

....

....

....

....

....

....

....

....

....

....

....

Activity 1

What type of research methods have been used to extract data in this article and other articles you have researched about this issue?

In your answer you should include:

- other methods of research used to explore the issue
- how reliable the results of the research methods used are.

Complete the guided answer below - this reflects one way of structuring an answer.

In your answer, show your understanding of **research methods** and the **validity** and **reliability** of **results** of the research. For example:

- Explain the research methods and show your understanding of qualitative methods for interpreting participant views, values and opinions.
- Explain the use of case studies and how these can be used to bring together findings to form triangulation.
- Support your evaluative judgements on suitability of methods.
- Show your understanding of any other research methods that are used in your secondary sources to explore the issue, such as quantitative (numerical data) that may support findings, e.g. numbers of families involved, level of funding.
- Support conclusions on reliability, showing an understanding of the concept in the context of the methods used.

> **Guided**

The purpose of the research was to explore the availability of sustainable childcare provision following government policy to extend free places to disadvantaged 2-year-olds, and what was planned by local authorities (LAs). The research conducted by Dickens, Wollny and Ireland (2012) used a qualitative approach that develops case studies based on ten local authorities. It looked at sufficiency assessments and the strategic planning of each local authority in the study together with the experiences and views of different types of childcare provider. These methods are appropriate where strategy and opinions are being sought.

The opening of the response draws on the notes prepared on the provided article. It starts by briefly introducing what the **research issue** was about, quickly moving on to identifying the qualitative **research methods**. It goes on to explain what the qualitative research methods used in the provided article were, why they were **suitable** and how they support **reliable results**.

Researchers analysed assessments of childcare availability produced by each local authority. They also carried out interviews with LA strategists to find how they intended to increase provision, improve quality, support financial sustainability and keep parents better informed. Interviews were carried out with group-based providers and childminders. To help researchers to understand factors that impacted on the sustainability of childcare provision researchers took into consideration the level of financial and other types of support they received from LAs. This ranged from Model 1 which included providers that were financially independent to Model 4 which included providers that were run by or reliant on LA funding. The choice of interviews was appropriate and reliable for their purpose. They helped researchers to gain a greater insight into the factors that were impacting on financial vulnerability and quality of provision than the use of questionnaires. More reliable outcomes were reached through triangulation of methods that included analysis of LA planning, and interviews with strategists and providers.

Parents' views were not sought through primary research but through a literature review. This meant that their perceptions were not current and could have changed, for example parents may have become better informed about provision in light of the policy to roll out free education to 2-year-olds.

You could go on to write about the qualitative methods used in **secondary research source 1**. You could discuss how information was gathered from local authorities, childcare professionals and other stakeholders. You could also discuss what the researchers were trying to find out and make a judgement about why this is the most effective method for examining case studies and exploring opinions and values.

You could consider the importance of involving LAs from different types of area, to include urban and rural. Also consider numbers and types of providers involved and come to a conclusion about the reliability of evidence. Comment on how parents were not interviewed. Note that the provided article refers to parents views, although using a literature review. Consider the reliability of the evidence in light of the note that the data collected by LAs was lacking in robustness and consistency (Gibb et al, 2011).

The research methods that were used in 'Rolling out free early education for disadvantaged

two year olds' (Gibb et al, 2011) were ....

....

....

....

....

....

....

....

....

....

....

....

Go on to write about the **research methods** used in your chosen **secondary research source 2** and how reliable the results of the research methods used are.

....

....

....

....

....

....

....

....

....

....

....

Your conclusion could sum up how reliable the results of the research methods used in the secondary research sources are as well as advantages and disadvantages, in relationship to the provided article and the issue.

....

....

....

....

....

....

....

....

....

....

Links Look at pages 103–107 of the Revision Guide to revise research methods and pages 140–142 to revise approaches to Activity 1.

Activity 2

Why is research into the sufficiency and sustainability of childcare provision in disadvantaged areas important for improving outcomes for children and their families?

In your answer to this question you should include how far your secondary research supports the conclusions drawn in the article.

> Complete the guided answer below - this reflects one way of structuring an answer.
>
> In your answer, show your understanding of the **relationship** between your own secondary research and the provided article, and how this relationship reinforces the **importance of the issue**.
>
> For example:
> - Analyse the issue, leading to conclusions about the issue's importance.
> - Provide relevant examples of possible effects on provision, including sufficiency, financial sustainability and quality, supported by research findings.
> - Explain the relationship between your secondary research findings and the issue in the article.
> - Show your understanding of the relationship between the two.

Guided

The research in the provided article conducted by Dickens, Wollny and Ireland (2012) shows the importance of research into sustainable, quality childcare provision in disadvantaged areas as outcomes can be improved for children and their families by reducing the gap in attainment between disadvantaged children and others of the same age by the time they start school. The research illustrates the importance of public funding and support for providers if they are to offer sufficient childcare places that meet the needs of disadvantaged families. With the roll out of free education to disadvantaged 2-year-olds there was increasing pressure for settings that could provide the required resources, experience and quality.

> The opening of this response explains what the research is about and the **importance of the issue** for disadvantaged children and their families. It includes references to the **provided article**.
>
> Continue the consideration of providers' concerns about raising or maintaining the quality of the early years provision following an increase in the numbers of 2-year-olds from disadvantaged families.

....

....

....

The research findings resulted in a better understanding of the factors that impacted on providers.

These included ....

....

....

> You could go on to draw on some of the data of the findings from secondary sources to justify your comments on the importance of the issue and show how far they support data and conclusions in the provided article.

In secondary research, I have found that flexibility in funding could help providers by ....

....

....

For example, the research by Gibb et al (2011) supports the conclusions drawn in the provided article and suggests funding childcare places over a whole year, rather than school terms, and offering additional funding, so providers didn't lose money where rates received for 2-year-olds may be lower than local rates/childcare fees.

The quality of provision varied between providers because some did not have experience of supporting disadvantaged children and families. These findings were reflected in the provided article

and show the importance of ....

....

....

....

....

....

> Remember that it is important to refer to both your secondary research sources and show **how far they support the conclusions in the provided article** about the importance of the research findings on how it affects outcomes for individual disadvantaged children and families. Provide examples and facts from the research to support your **objective response**. For example, research in both the provided article and secondary source 1 shows the importance of public funding for improving the number and quality of childcare places.
>
> Consider how secondary research source 2 relates to these conclusions and give any examples.

....

....

....

....

....

....

....

....

> Your conclusion could sum up how far your secondary resources **support the conclusions** in the provided article about why research like this is important for local authorities, providers, children and families, and comment on **reliability** of any **differing conclusions**.

....

....

....

....

....

....

....

....

....

....

....

....

....

....

....

Links Look at pages 98–100 of the Revision Guide to revise the importance of issues, page 123 for relationships between sources, and pages 143–144 for approaches to Activity 2.

Activity 3

What would you need to consider when planning your own primary research into provision for disadvantaged families?

The answer should refer to the article and your own secondary research.

> Complete the guided answer below – this reflects one way of structuring an answer.
>
> In your answer, show your understanding of **planning** and **ethical considerations** for further research, **supporting** any judgements made. For example:
> - Suggest research methods that could be used to continue investigation/exploration into the issue and give your reasons why.
> - Show your understanding of why the methods chosen are effective and suitable, and justify the choices.
> - Show your analysis skills.
> - Cover the planning considerations, ethical issues and necessary research skills required to explore the issue, showing your understanding of the practical problems of conducting research.

Guided ▷ The starting place for planning my own primary research into provision for disadvantaged families would be to consider any stated limitations in the research, or recommendations for further research, in the article and my own secondary research. For example, Dickens, Wollny and Ireland's study (2012) highlighted the importance of funding and support for improvements to childcare provision for children and families in disadvantaged areas. The interviews carried out in the research found agreement that sustainability of provision was affected by running costs, management and financial

skills, and accessibility. In my research ....

....

....

....

....

In the Dickens, Wollny and Ireland (2012) research, the perception of parents was not sought, relying instead on a literature review, which might be seen as limiting the research in terms of current perceptions. The literature review showed that parents in disadvantaged areas felt they had less information about provision than parents in advantaged areas. In light of that, further research could

....

....

....

> This answer outlines **future research needs**, including ways to **address possible limitations of current research** of the provided article. Go on to consider secondary source 1, and what this might mean for your future research plans.

My secondary research included specific exploration into the roll out of free education to disadvantaged 2-year-olds (Gibb et al 2011). The author noted in the findings that children's centres played a key role in the roll out but other providers lacked experience in supporting the needs of disadvantaged 2-years-olds and their families. This is interesting as it means that now that the roll out is in place, future research could be on whether funding and training has had the

necessary impact on different types of provision. ....

....

....

....

> You could go on to outline future research needs and plans in relation to secondary research source 2.

My secondary research also included ....

....

....

....

> You could move on to outline your overall future research plan. Make sure you justify your research plan to continue the exploration into the issue. Include planning considerations of the research methods and reliability, research skills required (those you have and those you need) and timescales to complete a piece of research.

To address the above, I would conduct further research using mixed methods, particularly into

....

....

....

To do this, I would need to design research that would extend or test the recommendations made.

My plan would be to ....

....

....

> As you continue, **justify** how your decisions on methods are suitable for reliable outcomes.

I would use a mix of quantitative and qualitative methods (mixed methods). I would implement and

observe the programme ....

....

....

I would also send questionnaires to parents about ....

....

For the quantitative side, I would establish data such as how many ....

....

> Go on to take account of **ethical considerations**, **justifying** how your decisions are suitable and effective for **reliable outcomes** (e.g. informed consent, permission to use settings, mental/physical capacity, data protection, legislation, recognised code of ethical conduct). Also, consider any **practical problems** you may encounter in your research, and how to overcome them.

It is important to ensure ethical procedures are followed so that participants do not experience harm, unfair treatment, are not given leading or incorrect information, etc. Ethical issues that need

to be considered for this research would be to ....

....

....

....

> Your conclusion could sum up possible strengths and limitations of your research plans.

....

....

....

> **Links** Look at pages 101–107 of the Revision Guide to revise planning research, pages 108–112 for ethical considerations, page 133 for future research, and pages 145–147 for approaches to Activity 3.

Activity 4

How can this research help early years settings to overcome difficulties that may impact on sufficiency and sustainability of quality provision for disadvantaged children and families?

Your answer should refer to the article and your own secondary research.

> Complete the guided answers below – this reflects one way of structuring an answer.
>
> In your answer, show your understanding of **research implications** for future provision and/or practice. For example:
> - Analyse and explain the implications of the research for provision/practice in the sector in a clear, orderly way.
> - Show your understanding of the implications of the issue in the context of the article and wider research.
> - Justify your recommendations for change.
> - Give supported reasons for implications.

> **Guided**

The research conducted by Dickens, Wollny and Ireland (2012) suggests that, to help early years settings overcome difficulties that may impact on sufficiency and sustainability of quality provision for disadvantaged children and families, childcare provision must be funded. The Gibb et al study (2011) focused on the need for funding that was flexible and tailored to local needs. It supports the conclusions of the importance of funding to ensure quality of provision that is effective in identifying and supporting the more complex needs of disadvantaged children and families. The research highlights a number of implications for practice and provision in relation to this. For example, staff could develop skills in securing and managing funding, and market what they offer. The use of best practice for quality provision could also attract funding and parents. Staff expertise could be improved through additional training to support the needs of disadvantaged children. The impact of early recognition of problems for children or families on practice and provision is that professionals can help put in place interventions that could have a significant impact on the outcomes for children. For example, supporting families in need may reduce the risk of abuse or neglect, reducing the cost for children's social and health services. Sufficient and quality provision can also help children to become school-ready, so reducing the education gap between them and more advantaged children.

> This answer starts by showing how **findings** from the provided article and secondary source 1 could impact on **provision** and **practice** in children's social and health services. Move on to show this in **relationship** to secondary source 2.

My further secondary research ....

....

....

....

....

....

....

....

Move into more detail to **analyse** and **explain** the **implications** of your research for provision and/
or practice. Consider how the different aspects of research might break down to **important parts**, and
address implications for practice and provision for each one systematically. For example, secondary source 1
provided research on strategies used to identify eligible families. You could consider the importance of this
for ensuring their engagement in the offer. Draw also on your knowledge of practice and provision of early
years settings in the context of the research sources and wider research. Remember to fully support the
implications by including references to all sources and giving reasons and examples.

....

....

....

....

....

....

....

You could consider the possible **advantages** and **disadvantages** in terms of implications of the research
on practice and provision. Why might an increase in the number of disadvantaged 2-year-olds affect the
organisation, training needs and staffing in settings? How can free education impact on outcomes for
children in later life? How can understanding other factors that may impact on a providers' financial stability
support improvement?

Give specific **examples** of the importance of **funding** and **support** for providers: what difference can it make
to levels of staffing, the environment and resources, and why is this important? What impact will this have on
quality and how will that attract more fee-paying parents to make the provision even more financially viable?

....

....

....

....

....

....

....

....

You could move ahead, in light of these implications, to summarise **key recommendations for change** in
practice and provision, making sure you **justify** your recommendations.

....

....

....

....

....

....

....

....

....

....

....

....

....

....

> **Links** Look at pages 131–132 of the Revision Guide to revise implications of research for practice and provision of services, and pages 148–149 to revise approaches to Activity 4.

END OF REVISION TASK

Answers

Unit 1: Children's Development
Revision paper 1 – guided (pages 2–13)

Section A

1 (a) **D** Picks up small objects using a pincer grasp
  (b) 3 Ruby can do up and undo her buttons, use a fork and spoon, turn the pages of a book, hop on one foot, run forwards and backwards and throw a ball.
  (c) Example answer:
   1 Chomsky's theory is based on the belief that language development is predetermined. He called this the Language Acquisition Device (LAD). This means that Ruby will develop her language naturally and will be able to use verbs and nouns in the correct order without being taught.
   2 Skinner's operant conditioning theory is based on the belief that children's language is a socially learned behaviour.
     Ruby's advanced language skills may be a sign that she has had language modelled and reinforced at home and at nursery.
  (d) Example answer:
   It is important that early years practitioners assess Sam's stage of numeracy development. Vygotsky refers to this as the Zone of Actual Development. Knowing what Sam can already do will help practitioners to plan how best to support Sam to reach the next stage. For instance, he can already add numbers to 10 so he could be helped to work with higher numbers and to look at patterns in numbers such as counting in twos or tens. Vygotsky refers to the next stage as the Zone of Proximal Development. This describes the stage that children can reach with the help of an adult or another child who is more skilled than them. In this way, Sam can be seen as an apprentice working alongside and learning from them. The adult should use different techniques, such as open-ended questioning, to help Sam to think about how to share or model thought processes to show how to work out change from 10p.

2 (a) 2 Powel will not have been able to express his needs and feelings through speech.
  (b) Example answer:
   1 Practitioners could use pictures of routines such as snack time to show alongside speech.
   2 Practitioners could use gestures, such as pointing, alongside speech to aid understanding.
  (c) Example answer:
   1 Bowlby suggests that a strong attachment between a child and the mother at an early stage influences attachments with others. This explains how Sofia is building a bond with her key person at nursery.
   2 According to Ainsworth, Sofia's reactions in being distressed when left by her mother, and happy at her mother's return, means that she has developed a secure attachment to her mother.
  (d) Example answer:
   Powel's and Sofia's experiences at home, including lifestyle and parenting, will have a direct influence on their growth and development. Now they have started nursery these experiences will also impact on their growth and development. For instance, they have more opportunity to socialise and be involved in cognitive play activity. Bronfenbrenner refers to these direct experiences as the microsystem. The relationship that is developed between these different experiences, such as meetings between the key person and Roza, will support the

children's development because there will be a shared understanding of their needs and the support they need. Bronfenbrenner identifies this influence as the mesosystem. The timing of transitions (chronosystem) will also impact on development. For example, because the children have started nursery shortly after moving to the UK, this may affect the children's ability to cope and possibly affect their emotional development.

3 (a) Example answer might be one of:
  • Amy does not have the ability to climb the climbing frame.
  • Amy is still using a palmar grasp to draw.
  (b) Example answer might be one of:
  • drinking alcohol
  • smoking.
  (c) Example answer:
   Amy will need strength in her large muscles, balance and coordination to be able to take part in physical play activity with friends. If she lacks these skills it may affect her ability to build friendships. Amy will need the ability to use the small muscles in her fingers and hand–eye coordination to be able to manipulate materials and resources in art activities.
  (d) Example answer:
   Continuous assessment is important to recognise when a child is not reaching their expected growth or developmental milestones. Once it has been recognised that Amy is not meeting expected norms in her physical development, practitioners can work together with Jasmine to plan activities that will help her. Assessment may indicate health problems or genetic conditions that require specialist treatment. Early recognition can ensure that medical or physiotherapy help is given at an early stage to prevent further problems. Delayed development in one area may impact on other areas of development. It may affect Amy's emotional and social development because it could cause her difficulty in joining in play with friends. She may get frustrated and upset if she cannot manage everyday tasks such as dressing.
   Her cognitive development could also be affected if she cannot take part in physical activities such as doing jigsaws or writing independently.
   The earlier that support is put into place by practitioners and, if necessary, specialists, the more likely it is to be effective.

4 (a) **B** Emotional
  (b) Two more examples from:
  • cramped conditions causing stress
  • lack of opportunity to play outdoors
  • few people left in the community.
  (c) Example answer:
   1 According to Bowlby, the first few weeks are critical for forming attachments with the mother. Separation at that time can affect Sara's emotional development.
   2 Bowlby suggests that poor attachments with the primary carer can affect how children form attachments later. This means that Sara may have difficulty in forming a bond with practitioners at playgroup.
  (d) Example answer:
   Sean is showing through his behaviour that the family's situation may have affected his emotions. If he is having difficulty in coping with his feelings, it can cause sleeping or eating problems. This can have an impact on Sean's health, growth and development. Sean may have low self-esteem, which could cause him to lose concentration

and interest in learning. This could prevent his continued cognitive development or even cause him to regress. Poor emotional development could result in a lack of confidence in his physical abilities and skills. If he does not take part in physical play he may lose some of his stamina, coordination and physical strength. Being aggressive to other children will lead to Sean becoming more and more isolated, which will mean that he will find it increasingly difficult to build friendships and relationships.

Section B

5 Answers may include the following:
- Children need opportunity for hands-on experience.
- Children think differently from adults.
- Children construct meaning and develop schemas from their experiences.
- Practitioners should provide experiences appropriate for children's age/stage of development.
- If children's experiences fit with their schema, they are in a state of equilibrium.
- Disequilibrium is caused by introducing new experiences.
- Children develop language through their ideas and experiences.
- As children explore, they assimilate their ideas/schemas.
- Criticisms suggest that children need the support of an adult to support learning.
- The early years curriculum should be planned to include child-initiated and adult-led activities.
- Planning for effective support must take into account a child's stage of development and readiness to learn.
- Planned activities and resources should give opportunity for children to learn through hands-on activity/exploration.

6 Answers may include the following:
- The role of the key person is:
  - to be the first point of contact for the child and parents
  - to get to know the child's needs, interests and routines
  - to provide security
  - to support transition
  - to be a role model for the child.
- Bowlby – the importance of a strong attachment to one key person, which provides a secure base for learning and holistic development.
- Bronfenbrenner – the influence of the child's environment and people in their life on development.
- Bronfenbrenner's mesosystem – how this explains the importance of interaction between home and nursery for positive development.
- Maslow's hierarchy of needs and the importance of understanding each child's basic needs and routines at home to provide for their needs in the setting.

Revision paper 2 (pages 14–23)

Section A

1 (a) **C** Can draw a detailed figure adding hair and eyes
  (b) Example answer:
   1 Poor nutrition may delay growth.
   2 Fewer opportunities for leisure restrict physical activity.
   3 Fewer opportunities for leisure may delay physical development.
  (c) Example answer:
   1 Aron will take part in play activities, such as role play or imaginative play, that require him to talk and negotiate with other children, and take turns when playing games.
   2 Aron will have the opportunity to take part in different activities that will help him to develop new skills, which will promote his self-image and self-esteem.
  (d) Answers may include the following:
   - A strong attachment in the early years is important for children to develop positive self-concept and self-esteem.

- Bowlby suggests that the attachment with the mother is the model for future attachments.
- A secure bond in the first year helps children to form positive relationships throughout life.
- Aron will feel more secure when he starts nursery because he starts from a safe and secure base.

2 (a) Two answers from the following:
   - Alesha will use simple sentences.
   - Alesha's speech can be understood.
   - Alesha will be asking questions.
  (b) Example answer:
   1 Give him words he can use to help him to express himself.
   2 Use art activities so that he can express feelings.
  (c) Example answer:
   1 Practitioners should understand the expected growth rates and milestones for each area of development so that they are able to recognise delays and put into place support at an early stage.
   2 Knowing the sequence of development means that practitioners can plan for and provide activities that will support Saeed to reach his next milestone.
  (d) Answers may include the following:
   - Naseem may feel insecure, which would affect his emotions.
   - He may feel worried that his mother may leave.
   - Anxiety and stress could affect his self-image and self-esteem.
   - Naseem may lose trust and have difficulty forming friendships and relationships.
   - Naseem may have difficulty sleeping, which will affect his learning and lower his self-esteem.
   - Naseem could show his frustration and anger through unwanted behaviour.

3 (a) **B** Bandura's social learning theory
  (b) Example answer:
   1 She can name common objects and actions such as 'car'.
   2 She knows around 50 words.
   3 She can link two words together.
  (c) Example answer:
   1 Connor will develop physical strength and stamina because he is using his gross motor skills to run around playing football and is using his strength to swing.
   2 Connor will develop coordination and balance when he uses the large muscles in his arms and legs to climb.
  (d) Answers may include the following:
   - Nature (a predisposition inherited from a parent) and nurture (experiences) influence neural development.
   - Brain development begins in the foetus and at birth Erin will already have 100 billion neurons.
   - Experiences in the first four years are critical for developing further connections between neurons, which are called neural pathways.
   - There are critical periods for the development of different parts of brain development in the early years.
   - At 3–4 months, early experiences will have helped neurological connections that developed Erin's senses.
   - At 9–10 months, connections are made in the part of the brain that supports the development of Erin's speech and language skills.
   - At 2 years, experiences and interactions are important for neurological connections that support the development of Erin's thought processes and higher level cognitive skills.

4 (a) Example answer:
   1 Sorting materials according to characteristics such as hard and soft.
   2 Water play with different shaped containers to find which holds more.

(b) Example answer:
1 Use stories to explore the feelings of characters that Pearl can identify with.
2 Model positive behaviour and point out when Pearl uses positive behaviour toward others.

(c) Example answer:
1 Pearl can be helped to make connections between words and objects or pictures when listening to stories, which will help her to recall the story later.
2 Using multi-sensory activities will help Pearl to process information so that she can recall it at a later date.

(d) Answers may include the following:
- According to Piaget's theory of stages of cognitive development, Pearl is in the pre-operational stage of cognitive development.
- Pearl is not yet reasoning or thinking logically.
- Pearl will explore her ideas symbolically through her role play, making one thing stand for another.
- Piaget also believed that children are egocentric at Pearl's age, which means she may want to lead the play and not listen to others' ideas.
- Critics of Piaget suggest that children can empathise with others at an earlier age.

Section B

5 Answers may include the following:
- Guided support can help a child to reach the next level of mathematical understanding.
- Children are apprentices who can learn through interaction with others.
- Vygotsky's Zone of Actual and Proximal Development for extending learning.
- Learning is an active process so children must be actively involved in the process alongside the adult.
- Close observation is important to plan for the next stage of mathematical development.
- Knowing the Zone of Actual Development that the child has reached is necessary to be able to plan for further development.
- Adult support helps children to reach the Zone of Proximal Development, which is a level they cannot reach alone.
- Using questioning and modelling mathematical language supports children to understand mathematical concepts.
- The development and use of language is important for cognitive development.

6 Answers may include the following:
- Skinner's operant conditioning theory.
- How the environment influences behaviour through reinforcers.
- The importance of using age-appropriate rewards.
- That positive or negative experiences influence whether the behaviour is repeated.
- The influence of negative reinforcement.
- The use of positive reinforcement.
- Bandura's social learning theory.
- The concept of modelling behaviour.
- That children copy unwanted as well as wanted behaviour.
- The importance of intrinsic motivation.
- That behaviour may be repeated because of a feeling of self-efficacy and empowerment.
- Criticisms of Skinner that rewards are extrinsic and may not work to shape behaviour in the long term.

Unit 2: Development of Children's Communication, Literacy and Numeracy Skills

Revision Activity 1 – Making notes

Read and understand the task and case study (page 26)
Example notes:

The setting and age groups of children
- The setting is part of a Foundation Stage Department and organised into two separate areas: a nursery for children aged 3 up to 4 years and a reception class for children aged 4 to 5 years.
- East Hill school has:
  ○ a group of 20 children who are between 4 and 5 years
  ○ a group of 24 nursery children half of which attend mornings only
  ○ children in nursery and reception class who have additional language needs
  ○ children whose home language is not English.

The reason for producing my report
- The purpose of my report is to make recommendations on ways to improve children's literacy outcomes by the time they reach 11 years and describe resources that will support their progress.
- The report must show how improvements link to best practice and theoretical approaches to reading to include synthetic phonics, analytical phonics and apprenticeship approach.

The audience for my report
The Foundation Stage Leader.

Additional learning needs, language needs or other considerations when writing my report
- Several children do not speak English at home.
- Four reception children and two nursery children have additional language needs.
- Outdoor activities need to meet the needs of children in both age groups.
- 12 nursery children attend mornings only – this may affect curriculum planning.

Structure and focus your notes (page 27)
Example notes:

Promote children's skills and abilities in reading and writing through daily adult-led activity
- Model reading and writing.
- Join in with role play and games.

Extend the use of theoretical approaches to reading across the staff team
- Synthetic phonics.
- Analytical phonics.
- Apprenticeship approach .

Make notes on literacy development and promoting reading and writing skills (page 28)
Example notes:
1 _Maximise opportunities for literacy development, indoors and outdoors, to include children with additional learning needs and those with a home language that is not English_
  - Staff should make sure that resources accessible to children are clearly labelled with a picture and word(s). There should be areas that are designated for reading and writing activities where children have a choice of materials. Displays must be at a suitable height for children to see and touch, well lit, include key words, attractive, be inside and outside.
  - Six play activities that can support children in developing reading and writing skill and abilities to include activities for an outdoor setting:
  Role play: post office/home/clinic; Story time; Art: painting/writing walls; Sand play: practising letter shapes; Computer software; Table top games.

- Resources needed that can support the identified play activities:
  Role play: telephones, note books, forms to fill in; Story time: large books, non-fiction and fiction, rhymes; Art: different colours and types of paper and writing materials; Sand play: Sand trays wet and dry; Computer software: programs for matching pictures/words; Table top games: lotto, dominoes, puzzles

2 Promote children's skills and abilities in reading and writing through daily adult-led activity.
- Three ways that staff can engage with children to promote reading and writing skills as they play:
  Annotate their pictures; Demonstrate handling books; Model hand writing.
- Advice to parents – three ways of supporting reading and writing skills at home:
  Advice on suitable books; Play word games; Point out words in the environment.

Make notes on extending use of theoretical approaches (page 29)

Example notes:

3 Extend the use of theoretical approaches to reading across the staff team
- Synthetic phonics approach supports children's understanding of phonemes (sounds) and graphemes (written letters). They are taught individually to enable children to segment words. The most common sounds are taught initially.
  - Advantages: children are able to sound out words at an early age, once phonemes are learnt they can be applied to unfamiliar words.
  - Disadvantages: some common words cannot be segmented easily; children may be able to read but not understand words in context.
- Analytical phonics supports children to blend sounds. They learn sets of words that have similar endings.
  - Advantages: children can use knowledge to apply to new words.
  - Disadvantages: many words are not spelled phonetically so rules learned cannot be applied.
- Apprenticeship approach/whole language approach. Children learn whole words rather than segmenting or breaking them down.
  - Advantages: children learn common words that are difficult to segment.
  - Disadvantages: there is a limit to how many words children can remember.

Make notes on theorists and theories (page 29)

Example notes:
- Vygotsky – social constructivism and how children can be supported to reach the next stage of development (Zone of Proximal Development). Children are able to achieve at a higher level when they are supported by an adult or a more able child.
- Bruner – the role of the adult critical for supporting their understanding and progressing to the next level.
- Piaget – children are active learners who need hands on activity to be able to construct their own understanding.

Revision Activity 1 – Making and justifying recommendations (pages 30–33)

Answers may include the following:

Report

This report has been produced by (your own name) and is intended for the Foundation Stage Leader of East Hill School.

Introduction

The purpose of this report is to make recommendations for improvements to the literacy skills of children attending the Foundation Stage Department, East Hill School.

Recommendations for a language-rich environment

The nursery and reception class must be organised to capture children's interest and curiosity about reading and writing. This can be achieved by a number of approaches. Staff should make sure that resources are clearly labelled with a picture and word(s). Displays must be labelled and include key words that children can use in their writing. Resource boxes should be labelled with pictures and words so that children whose home language is not English can access them independently.

There should be designated areas within the nursery and classroom for reading and writing activities. Resources and materials should be close by. Designated areas for reading and writing should be placed in well-lit areas where children can work away from noisy activity without disruption. Attractive displays with comfortable seating and floor or table spaces will encourage children to take part in activities.

Recommendations for activities that promote literacy, and required resources

It is recommended that children have opportunities to take part in the following play activities to promote their reading and writing skills:

- **Role play** should always be available. It should be changed regularly to include home, shop play and health clinic. These give opportunities for children to write, for example making lists or notes when using a telephone. They will become familiar with different forms of writing such as for displays, packaging, instructions and other children's notes.
- **Art activities**, including collage (cutting and sticking) and painting, must always be available to promote fine motor skills that are essential for the manipulation of writing materials and the development of handwriting.
- **Story time** should be part of the daily routine. By seeing common words and joining in with repetitive words, children will begin to recognise their shapes and be able to 'look and say' and link sounds to written symbols.
- **Table-top games** and puzzles should be provided each day to support visual discrimination.
- **Sand play** should be provided, indoors and outdoors, to give practice in forming letter shapes to support handwriting skills.
- **Computer programs** will support reading skills because children can both see and hear the sounds in the words that appear.

Resources and materials must be easily accessible to support activities.

They should include:
- a range of writing materials to include, markers, pencils, paints, paper, notebooks, painting walls that children can access and return to independently
- a range of different reading and picture books that are age appropriate to include rhymes and repetitive stories, and reading materials such as leaflets and posters
- computer word games that are age appropriate
- computers with word-processing programs and printers for children to write own stories.

The role of early years educators and parents to promote improvement in skills

Staff should engage with children in their role play and imaginative play. For example, helping to write a shopping list. They should join in with word games, helping children to match pictures with written words. Key words should be displayed in the room and pointed out to children. Phonic sounds should be introduced in order of usefulness for children and reinforced when sharing stories and rhymes. Staff should provide a range of books and reading materials, and demonstrate how to handle them. Staff should give children real reasons to write, such as recipes, letters or lists, and encourage children to label their work with their name and a description. Staff should write alongside children to model writing skills and demonstrate letter formation.

Parents can be advised on ways to support literacy at home by, for example, playing word games. They can point out words in the environment such as road names or shop signs. They could be given suggestions on suitable books at each age and stage and be encouraged to read with their children each day.

Theoretical approaches

Observation and assessment is critical for selecting the most appropriate method or methods for individual children. The synthetic phonic approach is most commonly used as it supports children's understanding of phonemes (sounds) and graphemes (writing). The advantages are that children learn different sounds quickly so that they can start to blend them when reading or segment them to write. This will give children confidence to read new words. However one criticism is that children may not understand meaning of words which they do not read in the context of the text. Analytical phonics will help children to learn words that have similar spellings. This approach helps children to apply what they have learned when they come across unfamiliar words for example jump, bump, that have the same endings. There are many English words that do not follow a regular pattern and cannot be read phonetically. Some children may benefit from a whole language approach, sometimes called the apprenticeship approach, through sharing books. Using this approach children learn the shape of whole words in the context of the text. This approach can support children to acquire knowledge of high frequency words that cannot be blended or learnt phonetically. The advantage is that children can associate words with pictures and understand them in the context of a sentence or story. The disadvantage of this approach is that the number of words that children can remember is limited and learning words as a whole does not help them to apply 'rules' to unfamiliar words.

Conclusion

The recommendations in this report will provide a balance between a language rich environment that provides literacy experiences and the support of early years' educators that reflects best practice. According to Piaget, hands on activities are important for children because they are active learners who need to construct their own meaning from their experiences. The adult role in observing, planning and supporting literacy is critical for ensuring children are provided with activities and resources that meet their individual needs and in providing effective support. Vygotsky's ZPD theory explains how children who are supported by an adult can achieve at a higher level of understanding than if they work alone. Similarly Bruner also stressed the importance of the adult interaction with children describing this process as 'scaffolding'. A curriculum that provides opportunities for language development and effective adult support is likely to improve outcomes for children at East Hill School.

Revision Activity 2 – Making notes

Read and understand the task and case study (page 34)

Example notes:

Information about Jakub and his family to help me identify a set of actions

- Jakub can communicate confidently in his home language.
- Jakub only hears Polish spoken at home.
- His father can speak a little English.
- His mother brings him to nursery but speaks no English.
- Jakub is isolated from other children.
- A member of staff speaks Polish.

Make notes to produce a set of actions (page 35)

Example notes:

Topic areas for producing a set of actions that can support Jakub and his family

- The role of the key person
- Stages of second language development
- Ways to include Jakub
- Jakub's interests
- Ideas for activities
- Resource ideas

Identify realistic goals (page 35)

Example notes:

Four realistic goals that adults should work toward to support Jakub in his development of English

- For Jakub to be able to understand and follow the routines at nursery.
- For Jakub to learn new vocabulary
- For Jakub to be able to join in/communicate with other children
- To involve Jakub's parents

Suggest actions (page 35)

Example notes:

One or two actions that can support Jakub to work toward each of the identified goals

- Display a visual timetable. Share the timetable with Jakub's parents.
- Use pictures alongside words. Speak clearly alongside gesture.
- Organise small group art activities.
- Use home/school diary in home language supported by Polish speaking member of staff. Encourage Jakub to take home art work.

Resources and the role of the adult (page 36)

Example notes:

Resources needed to support the actions suggested

- A visual timetable showing the key events of the day to include lunchtime, story time, home time etc.
- Materials written in Polish
- A range of art materials
- Home/school diary supported by members of staff

The role of the early years educator and Jakub's parents in supporting actions

The early years educator should:

- point to the visual image on the timetable to help Jakub to make links between words and events, e.g. snack time and sitting on the carpet and sharing fruit
- use gestures alongside words when giving instructions
- involve parents with help of Polish speaking member of staff.

Jakub's parents should:

- meet regularly with his key person with the help of an interpreter
- share information through a home/school diary
- understand the routines of nursery
- share games and books that can be played at home.

Links with early years theory (page 37)

Example answer:

Three early years theories to explore best practice in supporting the development of second language skills and abilities

- Vygotsky emphasised the importance of social interaction for language development. This can be with adults or children who have skills in what is being learnt.
- Bruner stressed the importance of the adult supporting the child so they can progress. He referred to this support as 'scaffolding' children's learning.
- Bowlby's attachment theory explains the importance of secure attachments. The key person role will help Jakub to build effective attachments, essential for him to be able to integrate and develop his language skills.

Activity 2 – Producing a set of actions (pages 38–40)

Answers may include the following:

Background

Jakub is 3 years old. He is proficient in his home language. He has just joined the nursery and has no understanding of English. He speaks Polish with his family at home.

Introduction

The purpose of this set of actions is to help Jakub to settle into the nursery. He will feel more settled if he understands and is supported to follow the routines at nursery. As Jakub enjoys art activities, these activities could be used to support him to acquire English. Jakub appears to be isolated. Helping him to join in with other children could support his language. It is important that Jakub's home language is acknowledged and supported alongside developing English.

Set of actions

The following set of actions will support Jakub to settle in to the nursery and begin to acquire English:

- Display a visual timetable and share the timetable with Jakub's parents.
- State clearly what is happening and support with gesture before each change of routine.
- Engage with Jakub during a painting activity, introducing new words.
- Encourage Jakub to take artwork home to share with parents.
- Play visual or table-top games or computer programs that are easy to follow with Jakub and one or two selected children.
- Engage in play with Jakub, such as being a customer in shop play.
- Involve the Polish-speaking member of staff in interactions with Jakub's mother to help to explain what he has been doing.

Resources to support actions

- Produce a visual timetable depicting the main events of the day, to include lunchtime, story time and home time.
- Provide materials for art activities.
- Provide a range of pictorial games such as lotto, dominoes, computer programs.
- Provide storybooks or rhymes written in Polish.

Adult role

The early years practitioner should point to the appropriate visual image on the timetable each time the routine changes to help Jakub to make links between the words and events, such as 'snack time' and sitting on the carpet to share fruit. They could learn a few key words in Polish. The early years practitioner should engage in play with Jakub by giving simple, clear instructions supported by non-verbal communication. The early years practitioner should observe Jakub closely to find out what he enjoys doing and provide regular activities such as art. They should carefully plan groupings so that Jakub can play effectively with other children. It is important that they work in partnership with Jakub's parents with the support of an interpreter. If possible, information about the curriculum and organised events should be provided in Polish. Jakub's parents should be encouraged to support Jakub in his home language. They should explain the nursery routines to Jakub in Polish so that he recognises and understands the visual timetable. They could complete a nursery/home diary that can be interpreted by a Polish-speaking member of staff.

Conclusion

The set of actions are important for helping Jakub to settle into the nursery and to acquire English. Identifying a key person to support him and to be the first point of contact for his parents will help to do this as he will feel more secure and be able to form an attachment. Bowlby's attachment theory helps to explain the importance of building secure attachments for children's emotional and social development.

Both Vygotsky, and later Bruner, emphasised the importance of social interaction for promoting children's cognitive and language development. This means that it is important that the practitioner engages with him and also encourages his play with other children. Engaging with Jakub and scaffolding him as he begins to develop English is critical for supporting Jakub's acquisition of English.

Revision Activity 3 – Making notes

Read and understand the task and activities you need to design (page 41)

Example answer:

Topic areas that are useful for producing a plan of each activity
- An outline for an activity plan
- Ideas for measurement activities with links to curriculum objectives
- The needs of individual children
- Strategies for supporting children's learning
- How resources can be used
- Theories that help to explain how children are learning

Identify headings you will need in each activity plan (page 41)

Example answer:

Additional headings could include:
- Additional needs
- Learning goals/objectives
- Description of activity
- Mathematical terminology
- Support by adult
- Justification/conclusion

Identify learning goals (page 42)

Example answer:

What children must learn about measurements (learning goals)
- Ordering objects according to their length
- Using balance scales to identify objects that weigh more or less than a given object
- Using natural materials to compare/order capacity
- Measuring periods of time using non-standard measures, e.g. sand timers
- Solving problems relating to length, weight, capacity.
- Introduction to standard measures

Suggest two activities (page 42)

Example answer:

Two activities to support children working towards learning goals about measurement, with linked terms.

Activity 1

Comparing objects by weight and using balance scales to order them according to their weight.

Mathematical terms: heavier than, lighter than, balance, weight.

Activity 2

Measuring length, using strides (non-standard measures) and discussing reasons for differences in results. Using standard measures and discussing why results are the same.

Mathematical terms: length, measure, standard measure, metres, how many, same, different.

Roles and individual needs (page 43)

Example answer:

Four ways that the early years educator, adults or others can support each activity.
- Asking open-ended questions to promote thinking
- Modelling activity
- Using commentary
- Checking understanding

Individual support for children with hearing loss and language delay
- For children who have language delay adults should make sure they have eye contact. Speech should be clear and short sentences used. Use non-verbal communication alongside verbal when giving instructions.
- For children with hearing loss the adult should make sure the child is sitting facing them. The adult should also use gesture and pictures alongside words.

Links with early years theories (page 43)

Example answer:

<u>Three theorists and their theories that can help to justify the practice described in the activities to support children's learning</u>

- Piaget – links to activities that provide opportunities for 'hands on' measuring activities that enable children to construct their understanding.
- Vygotsky – Zone of Proximal Development (ZPD). The role of the adult to support and guide children in their learning which enables them to achieve at a level that they may not do alone.
- Bruner – describes the process in which adults support children in their learning as 'scaffolding'. He recognised the importance of the role of the adult in engaging with children to progress their cognitive development.

Activity 3 – Producing two activities (pages 44–48)

Answers may include the following:

Activity Plan 1

<u>Age and group</u>
A group of six reception class children aged 4–5 years

<u>Additional needs</u>
This activity takes into account the needs of:
- one child with hearing loss
- two children with language delay.

<u>Learning goals</u>
By taking part in this activity children will:
- understand the terms heavier and lighter
- be able to compare two objects
- be able to order objects by weight.

<u>Description of activity</u>
The activity will be delivered to children working in a group of six.
- Make sure that children are sitting in a small circle facing you. This will help the child with hearing loss and children with language delay to understand what you say.
- Begin by showing the children the objects of different weights. Pass each object around the group so that each child can handle it. Say the name of the object clearly as they hold it and repeat for children with additional communication needs. Ask children to predict if each object is heavy or light and then ask children to say if it is heavy or light as they handle it.
- Get children to work in pairs to sort objects into boxes labelled heavy and light. Get them to talk about their reasons for sorting. Ask children to find which object is the lightest. Get them to think about how to do this but if they are not sure suggest using the balance scale.
- Ask children to order the objects from lightest to heaviest and record what they have done. They can draw and label or just draw the objects, depending on their literacy skills.
- Extend the activity by asking children to check their decisions using cubes to balance.

<u>Resources</u>
The activity will take place in a quiet area of the classroom around a circular table that seats six children.
Resources may include:
- three sets of objects of different weights to include heavy and lighter such as a large smooth pebble, a fir cone, an apple, a can of beans, a feather, a pencil, a glue stick, a plastic toy
- three sets of balance scales
- cubes for balancing.

<u>Role of the adult</u>
Questioning – ask open-ended questions to develop thought and problem-solving skills, such as 'why do you think that object is heavier? How could you check which one is heavier and which is lighter?' Use commentary as children work, such as 'I see that you are using cubes to check how many balance the pebble.' Modelling by demonstrating ways to check which object is heavier or lighter. Use repetition of key words that children should learn, to include

heavier, lighter, balance. Use praise to encourage children. Observe children's actions and responses to check understanding. Repeat or rephrase instructions for children with additional communication needs.

<u>Justification for activity plan</u>
This plan will help to develop children's understanding of the concept of heavier and lighter. They will have to problem solve when working out ways to compare and order the objects. Engaging with children through questioning and modelling will encourage higher thinking skills, a process described by Bruner as 'scaffolding'. It also gives them opportunity for hands on activity which Piaget believed critical for children to develop new concepts. Children with hearing loss will be included because they are using their sense of sight as well as hearing. The recording activity, which may involve drawing or writing, is adapted to meet the needs of individual children. The activity plan can meet the needs of children at different ability levels as they can sort by heavy/light and more able children will order by weight.

Activity Plan 2

<u>Age and group</u>
Reception class children aged 4–5 years.
Work with groups of four to six children.

<u>Additional needs</u>
This activity takes into account the needs of:
- one child with hearing loss
- two children with language delay.

<u>Learning goals</u>
By taking part in this activity children will:
- be able to measure length and distance using non-standard and standard measures
- understand the need for standard measures
- use the terms standard measure and metre
- develop skills in measuring distance.

<u>Description of activity</u>
Take children into the play area and ask them to take strides across and count each stride. Get them to write down the number of strides on a large sheet of paper next to their name in the first column.
Prompt them to think why children may have recorded different lengths/numbers. Tell children that the builders needed to put down a new surface and need to know the exact measurement. Ask children how they could make sure the measurement was correct.
Show children a measuring wheel and demonstrate against a metre rule how each turn measures one metre. Ask each child in turn to walk across the play area and count how many turns. Get them to record the number in the second column. Ask children to say why the number of metre measures is the same.
Children could go on to measure the width of the area and record non-standard and standard measures.

<u>Resources</u>
- a rectangular outdoor play area or marked area of around 10 metres
- sheets of poster paper with the names of children listed and two columns
- marker pens
- distance measuring wheel

<u>Role of adult</u>
- Use open-ended questioning such as 'why did you take more strides than your friend?'
- Demonstrate taking strides and the use of the measuring wheel.
- Record results of your own strides.
- Observe children's actions and responses to check understanding. Make sure that children are facing you when giving instructions, and repeat or rephrase for children with additional communication needs.
- Model counting strides, if children are unsure, by walking and counting with them.

Justification for activity plan

Children are actively involved in the activity, which reflects best practice in early years. According to Piaget this will help children to construct their understanding of new concepts. The activity is a practical demonstration of the importance of standard measures. By comparing the results from using non-standard and standard measures, children are helped to understand this concept. Adults who support children in this way will, according to Vygotsky, help them to achieve a level of understanding and use skills which they are not able to do alone. The activity will also develop skills in measuring, and through practical demonstration the adult can involve children who have language delay and hearing loss. It is an effective activity for introducing standard measures before children go on to use centimetres.

Unit 4: Enquiries into Current Research in Early Years Practice

Revision task

1 Research (pages 50–76)

Plan and monitor your research (page 50)

Stages of research

1	Read and annotate the article
2	Familiarise myself with the article, making notes and identifying issues
3	Note key words on the content of the article, in order to search for secondary research sources
4	Search and note possible sources for secondary research, based on the content of the article
5	Assess reliability of secondary source 1, chosen with reference to **S**ource, **A**ppearance, **M**ethods, **T**imeliness, **A**pplicability and **B**alance (**SAMTAB**)
6	Make focused bullet notes on secondary research source 1, including a focus on methods, reliability, ethics, importance of issue, further research (e.g. proposal, timing, ethics), impact of research on practice and provision. Show the links in relationship to the provided article
7	Assess reliability of secondary source 2 using the approach outlined in 5 above
8	Make focused bullet notes on secondary source 2 as outlined in 6 above

Read and annotate the article (page 51)

Your own annotations.

Familiarise yourself with the article (page 58)

Example notes:

1 What was the research piece about?
   - Timing and subject of study important because from 2013 free pre-school provision, already in place for 3–4 year olds, was due to extend to disadvantaged two year olds.
   - Free provision introduced because previous research showed that quality provision can reduce gap in attainment between disadvantaged children and others of the same age by the time they start school.
   - Research was carried out in order to understand local authority strategy relating to early years provision.
   - Researchers wanted to understand how local authorities were responding to change in policy and whether it was possible for them to support increased demand.
   - More specifically, they wanted to find out whether provision is sufficient for disadvantaged children and families in the chosen local authority areas and to explore whether it is financially sustainable.

   - Researchers also wanted to look at quality of provision and whether it could meet the particular needs of disadvantaged children and their families.
   - This required them to understand parents' childcare needs and the level of their knowledge and understanding about access and availability of provision.
   - To achieve these aims researchers investigated the strategic planning of local authorities, current provision and views of parents.

2 What were the key methods used in the research?
   - Study used qualitative methods, appropriate where strategy and opinions are being sought.
   - Case study approach was used based on the experiences of different types of provision across ten local authorities.
   - Local authority (LA) sufficiency assessments were analysed and LA strategists were interviewed.
   - Literature review looked at the level of demand, needs and perceptions of parents in disadvantaged areas.
   - Interviews were carried out with different types of pre-school providers within each of the LAs.
   - Different models of provision were identified depending on level of government funding received.
   - These ranged from Model 1, being settings that are self-sufficient and rely on parents paying fees, to Model 4, which included authority run, authority-funded and supported settings.
   - Triangulation of different methods led to reliable outcomes, through analysing LA assessments, speaking directly to LA strategists and interviewing a range of types of pre-school provision with different funding levels, enabling them to draw conclusions on the capacity to offer and sustain places.
   - Interviews help researchers to interpret and understand participant responses.
   - Although not UK-wide this could be considered sufficient to come to a conclusion about the current state of provision.

3 What were the key findings in the research?
   Researchers reached five key conclusions from their research:
   1 Provision in disadvantaged areas: There were sufficient places to meet increased demand but providers experienced financial difficulty and needed funding in order to be sustainable.
   2 In disadvantaged areas where providers were subsidised and supported by the LA, provision was shown to be of higher quality.
   3 The strategy of local authorities focused on increasing the number of places in existing group-based settings and childminders, increasing sustainability and improving quality.
   4 Providers in disadvantaged areas were reliant on funding for several reasons including: lower demand for fee-paying provision/difficulties in keeping fees down; increased running costs; the needs of the local people, e.g. if they were constantly moving; their attitudes to childcare; accessibility; local competition.
   5 Providers were supportive of the policy to extend free childcare to disadvantaged 2-year-olds but believed it was not possible to offer the quality of childcare that was required if they had to rely on market forces. Reasons given were different across the different types of childcare.
      - Private providers felt it may not be worthwhile financially.
      - Voluntary and independent providers would need funding to help them to make premises suitable to take in more children, train the workforce and increase ratios for 2-year-olds
      - Childminders were concerned about additional paperwork involved in the care of 2-year-olds.
      - Parents preferred other types of provision to childminders.
   There was commitment to supporting policy to roll out free education to 2-year-olds but there were factors impacting on the financial stability and sustainability of providers.

4 Were any recommendations/future research plans discussed?
- Although the study does not give specific recommendations it highlights concerns and challenges.
- Concerns raised about sufficiency and quality of places indicate further research may be needed on ability of providers to meet possible additional parental support, and communication, language and care needs of children.
- Ten local authorities provided a substantial sample although researchers felt they could not generalise evidence across other LAs.
- When interviewed, strategists and providers were in agreement that sustainability of provision was affected by a number of different factors such as running costs, management skills, accessibility.
- Any or all of these issues could also lead to further research.
- Parents' perceptions were not sought through interview or questionnaire as with other key stakeholders, instead relying on a literature review, meaning that views in relation to the new policy of free education for 2-year-olds were not taken into account.
- Literature review found that parents in disadvantaged areas felt they had less information about childcare than those in advantaged areas (Speight, 2010, as cited in Dickens, Wollny and Ireland, 2012).
- Local authorities planned to improve information to parents so a useful piece of future research might be to find if this had improved parents' knowledge and resulted in flexibility to meet needs such as fitting with changing working patterns, training staff in areas of additional needs, understanding different cultures.
- This might result in improved and targeted funding and LA support for preferred types of provision.

5 What could be the implications/impact on your practice?
- Research findings for this study helps providers to be aware of issues that could impact on their setting if taking on 2-year-olds.
- Implications for my own practice are that I would need to be prepared for changes or it could impact on my job security, pay or availability of work.
- Need additional training to meet the needs of 2-year-olds and to support disadvantaged children and their families who may have more complex needs.
- High-quality setting would need to use best practice, to attract fee-paying parents and LA funding.
- Need to be familiar with policy, to advise parents, and develop management skills/strategies to improve financial sustainability of the setting.

6 What could the implications/impact be on early years provision?
- Study highlights four different models of provision that local authorities can positively address, using improved financial management and marketing of their setting.
- Widening provision in disadvantaged areas to include 2-year-olds may mean reorganisation and additional resources to meet different needs.
- Quality provision which ensures a higher Ofsted rating may attract more fee-paying parents.
- Long-term educational/social benefits will follow as a result of earlier recognition of needs.
- This may reduce later interventions and save time/costs to professional early years services.

Note key words for searching for secondary sources (page 61)
Key words for an internet search for secondary sources, based on the provided article
Example answer:
There are a number of different terms you could use to search for secondary research sources. The inclusion of Boolean operators and use of specific terms can provide a better focus than more generic terms:

- take-up of free early years education
- costs and childcare
- early years policy
- evaluation of free early education

Search and note possible sources (page 62)
Your own responses.

Make notes on secondary research source 1 (page 68)
4 Were any recommendations/future research plans discussed?
Continuation of notes might include the following:
Types of method and reliability
- In-depth interviews with providers and early years staff with more in-depth analysis of their experience in supporting families, how they work in partnership, and training needs.
- Continue with the qualitative methods, but introduce some quantitative research, for example funding levels and numbers of disadvantaged 2-year-olds taking up free places.
- Own responses for choice of quantitative/qualitative methods matched to purposes.

Relationship to the provided article
- Use the data from above to inform research on improvements to the quality and sufficiency of provision that can meet the needs of disadvantaged families.
- Own responses for detail of the research.

Limitations in current research to address in future research
- Stakeholders were involved but this did not include parents' perceptions on how they were informed and engaged, and the quality and flexibility of provision. Extend research into how quality of provision is measured and parents' perceptions.
- Own responses for detail of the research plan.

Planning
your own response in relations to planning research, such as ethical considerations, safeguarding issues, informed consent using appropriate methods, confidentiality and data protection; research skills required (those you have and those you need); possible problems and how to overcome them; timeline for research, taking into account, e.g. holidays, illness, etc; timeline and framework for the research, e.g. updated research figures, trends and predictions.

Research literature
Your own suggestions for literature review that might include the guidelines noted in relation to the sustainability of provision in disadvantaged areas/needs of children and parents/issues around staffing/partnership working/quality and implications for future research, practice and provision.

5 **What could be the implications/impact on practice?**
Your own notes, as appropriate for individual setting and practice.

6 **What could the implications/impact be on early years provision?**
Your own notes.

Complete a SAMTAB and notes on secondary research source 2 (page 71)
Your own notes as appropriate f*or the chosen secondary research source 2.*

Provide a list of the secondary sources you have used in addition to the provided article (page 74).

2 Revision activities (pages 76–88)

Details to be taken from notes on page 76, with own response, based on chosen sources.

Activity 1 (page 77)
Continuation of answer might include the following:
Quantitative methods used in secondary source 1:
- The source states there was a case study approach using in-depth interviews with local authorities, stakeholders and providers.
- The methods helped researchers to look in depth at how eligible families were identified, how the roll out of the offer was being managed by local authorities to ensure support and quality of provision, and the experiences of providers.

- The case studies involved local authorities with different levels of deprivation, which made findings more reliable.
- Researchers noted that some local authorities were less effective in monitoring the effects of the roll out to 2-year-olds so this may have impacted on the findings.

Research methods used in secondary source 2:

Your own response, based on chosen sources.

Conclusion:

Your own response, based on chosen sources.

Activity 2 (page 80)

Continuation of answer might include the following:

- Reference to the explanations in the conclusion to the provided article on how the issue is important.
- How the research issue may impact on the outcome for children and their families, providers and local authorities.
- References to the support and funding given by local authorities and how it impacts on sustainability of different types of provision which may impact on parental choice.
- The importance of financial sustainability for improvements in staffing, resources and quality of provision.
- How each study highlights the additional/particular needs of disadvantaged children and families that require additional expertise/funding.
- How financial concerns can impact on the flexibility of provision which is demanded by families.
- How findings of your secondary sources link to the provided article and whether there are any similarities that support the findings in the provided article, and reliability if there are differing conclusions. Indicate the importance of findings to disadvantaged children and their families, to providers, and to local authorities, and provide examples.

Activity 3 (page 83)

Your own response, based on chosen sources.

Activity 4 (page 86)

Your own response, based on chosen sources.

Notes